Stories
about Sets

ACADEMIC PAPERBACKS*

EDITED BY Henry Booker, D. Allan Bromley, Nicholas DeClaris,
W. Magnus, Alvin Nason, and A. Shenitzer

BIOLOGY

Design and Function at the Threshold of Life: The Viruses
  HEINZ FRAENKEL-CONRAT
The Evolution of Genetics ARNOLD W. RAVIN
Isotopes in Biology GEORGE WOLF
Life: Its Nature, Origin, and Development A. I. OPARIN
Time, Cells, and Aging BERNARD L. STREHLER
The Spread of Cancer JOSEPH LEIGHTON

ENGINEERING

A Vector Approach to Oscillations HENRY BOOKER
Dynamic Programming and Modern Control Theory RICHARD
  BELLMAN and ROBERT KALABA
Hamilton's Principle and Physical Systems B. R. GOSSICK

MATHEMATICS

Finite Permutation Groups HELMUT WIELANDT
Complex Numbers in Geometry I. M. YAGLOM
Elements of Abstract Harmonic Analysis GEORGE BACHMAN
Geometric Transformations (in two volumes) P. S. MODENOV
  and A. S. PARKHOMENKO
Introduction to p-Adic Numbers and Valuation Theory
  GEORGE BACHMAN
Linear Operators in Hilbert Space WERNER SCHMEIDLER
The Method of Averaging Functional Corrections: Theory and
  Applications A. Yu. LUCHKA
Noneuclidean Geometry HERBERT MESCHKOWSKI
Quadratic Forms and Matrices N. V. YEFIMOV
Representation Theory of Finite Groups MARTIN BURROW
Stories about Sets N. Ya. VILENKIN
Commutative Matrices D. A. SUPRUNENKO and
  R. I. TYSHKEVICH

PHYSICS

Crystals: Their Role in Nature and in Science CHARLES BUNN
Elementary Dynamics of Particles H. W. HARKNESS
Elementary Plane Rigid Dynamics H. W. HARKNESS
Mössbauer Effect: Principles and Applications
  GUNTHER K. WERTHEIM
Potential Barriers in Semiconductors B. R. GOSSICK
Principles of Vector Analysis JERRY B. MARION

*Most of these volumes are also available in a cloth bound edition.

STORIES
ABOUT SETS

N. Ya. Vilenkin

Translated by SCRIPTA TECHNICA

ACADEMIC PRESS New York and London

ACADEMIC PRESS INC.
111 Fifth Avenue, New York, New York 10003

United Kingdom Edition published by
ACADEMIC PRESS INC. (LONDON) LTD.
Berkeley Square House, London W.1

Library of Congress Catalog Card Number: 66-30111

PRINTED IN THE UNITED STATES OF AMERICA

First published in the Russian language under the title

RASSKAZY O MNOZHESTVAKH

by

IZDATEL'STVO "NAUKA"
GLAVNAYA REDAKTSIYA FIZIKO-MATEMATICHESKOĬ LITERATURY
Moscow, 1965

Foreword

Professor Vilenkin has produced a small masterpiece which can be read with profit and delight by anybody, beginning with high school juniors and seniors. Slightly more than half of the book explores the notion of cardinality of sets and the remainder traces the evolution of some of the most important concepts of mathematics such as function, curve, surface, and dimension. The exposition combines informality with integrity of presentation and there is a wealth of unusual examples illustrating the paradoxical properties of curves and surfaces. It is safe to say that Professor Vilenkin's essay provides a royal road to the important concepts with which it is concerned.

A. SHENITZER

January, 1968
Adelphi University
Garden City, New York

Preface

I first had occasion to hear of the theory of sets at a lecture conducted by I. M. Gel'fand for Moscow school children. He was then just beginning his teaching career, but is now a corresponding member of the Academy of Sciences of the USSR. During the course of two hours he told us about what seemed to us to be completely improbable things: that there are just as many natural numbers as there are rational numbers, and that there are just as many points in an interval as there are in a square.

My acquaintance with the theory of sets was further developed during my time as a student of mathematics and mechanics at the Moscow State University. In addition to the lectures and seminars, we had our own ways of learning, ways that our professors and lecturers probably did not even suspect. After class (and sometimes, I must confess, even during class, if the lecture was not especially interesting) we wandered through the corridors of the old building on Mokhovoi Street and discussed interesting problems, surprising examples, and clever proofs. In these conversations, for example, the first-year students learned from their more experienced fellows how to construct a curve which passes through all the points of a square, or how to find a function which has a derivative nowhere, and so forth.

Of course, the explanations given were, so to speak, "out of bounds," and it would be considered a mark of inexcusable frivolousness if you went to take an exam after having listened to these discussions. No, really, there was no talk of exams—according to the course of study, we would not be taking "real variables" for two more years. But, then, how this "corridor" preparation helped in taking exams and understanding lectures! For each of the theorems we could recall interesting problems which we had to solve earlier, perceptive juxtapositions, and intuitive examples.

I want to tell the reader about the theory of sets in the same way, in which I learned it, by following the "corridor" course of study. Thus, our attention will be focused mainly on giving clear presentations of problems, discussing unexpected or surprising examples, quite often giving contradictory "naive" discussions. We shall find that the theory of functions of a real variable is richly endowed with all these. And if, after he has read this book, a high-school or college student wants to study the theory of sets or the theory of functions of a real variable more deeply, the author will feel that his book has been a success.

Of the many standard presentations of these subjects, the following are recommended:

1. A. N. Kolmogorov and S. V. Fomin, "Measure, Lebesgue Integrals, and Hilbert Space" (Book II of "Elements of the Theory of Functions and Functional Analysis," translated by N. A. Brunswick and A. Jeffrey). Academic Press, New York, 1961.

2. I. P. Natanson, "Theory of Functions of a Real Variable," Vol. 1, edited by Leo F. Boron and Edwin Hewitt, 1955. Vol. 2, edited by Leo F. Boron, 1959. Ungar, New York.

3. F. Hausdorff, "Set Theory," 2nd ed. Chelsea, New York, 1967.

Much interesting information about some of the problems touched upon here can be found in the book of A. S. Parkhomenko "Chto takoe liniya."

Some problems from the theory of functions of a real variable are given at the end of the book; the reader will find it helpful to attempt their solution.

Contents

4. Remarkable Functions and Curves, or a Stroll through a Mathematical Art Museum

1

Some Extraordinary Properties of Infinite Sets

It would not be an exaggeration to say that all of mathematics derives from the concept of infinity. In mathematics, as a rule, we are not interested in individual objects (numbers, geometric figures), but in whole classes of such objects: *all* natural numbers, *all* triangles, and so on. But such a collection consists of an *infinite* number of individual objects.

For this reason mathematicians and philosophers have always been interested in the concept of infinity. This interest arose at the very moment when it became clear that each natural number has a successor, i.e., that the number sequence is infinite. However, even the first attempts to cope with infinity lead to numerous paradoxa.

For example, the Greek philosopher Zeno used the concept of infinity to prove that motion was impossible! Indeed, he said, for an arrow to reach its target it must first cover half the distance to the target. But before it can cover this half, it has to cover a fourth, an eighth, etc. Since the process of halving is a never-ending one (here infinity crops up!), the arrow never leaves the bow. He proved in an identical fashion that swift Achilles never overtakes the slow tortoise.

Fɪɢ. 1.   Achilles and the tortoise.

Because of these paradoxa and sophisms, the ancient Greek mathematicians refused to have anything to do with the notion of infinity and excluded it from their mathematical arguments. They assumed that all geometric figures consisted of a finite number of minute, indivisible parts (atoms). With this assumption, it turned out to be impossible, for instance, to divide the circle into two equal parts—the center would have to belong to one of the two parts, but this would contradict their equality.

In the Middle Ages the problem of infinity was of interest mainly in connection with arguments about whether the set of angels who could sit on the head of a pin was infinite or not. A wider use of the notion of infinity began in the 17th century, when mathematical analysis was founded. Concepts such as "infinitely large quantity" and "infinitely small quantity" were used in mathematical reasoning at every step.   However, sets containing infinitely many elements were not studied at this time; what were studied were quantities which varied in such a way as eventually to become larger than any given number. Such quantities

FIG. 2. How many angels can sit on the head of a pin?

were called "potentially infinitely large," meaning that they could become as large as you please (potentia: possibility).

It was only in the middle of the 19th century that the study of infinite sets, consisting of an infinitely large number of elements, began to occur in the analysis of the concept of infinity.   The founders of the mathematical theory of infinite sets were the Czech savant B. Bolzano (unfortunately, his main work was not published until many years after his death in 1848) and the German mathematician Georg Cantor. It is a curious fact that both founders of the theory of sets were well acquainted with the science of the Scholastics. But they were able to improve on the Scholastics and turn the theory of sets into an important part of mathematics.

The chief attainment of Bolzano and Cantor was the study of the properties of infinite sets; the properties of finite sets were well known by their predecessors. It turned out that the properties of finite and infinite sets were completely dissimilar: many operations impossible for finite sets could be carried out with ease for infinite sets. For example, try to find room in an already full hotel for an additional guest, if it is assumed that each room cannot have more than one occupant. It can't be done? This is only because the number of rooms in a hotel is finite! But if there were an infinite number of rooms. . . . Such hotels *can* be found in the stories about the interstellar traveler Ion the Quiet, the famous hero of "The Interstellar Milkman, Ion the Quiet," written by the Polish fantasist Stanislaw Lem. Let's hear what he has to say.

The Extraordinary Hotel, or the Thousand and First Journey of Ion the Quiet

I got home rather late—the get-together at the club Andromeda Nebula dragged on long after midnight. I was tormented by nightmares the whole night. I dreamt that I had swallowed an enormous Kurdl; then I dreamt that I was again on the planet Durditov and didn't know how to escape one of those terrible machines they have there that turn people into hexagons; then .... People generally advise against mixing old age with seasoned mead. An unexpected telephone call brought me back to reality. It was my old friend and companion in interstellar travels Professor Tarantog.

"A pressing problem, my dear Ion," I heard. "Astronomers have discovered a strange object in the cosmos—a mysterious black line stretching from one galaxy to another. No one knows what is going on. Even the best telescopes and radio-telescopes placed on rockets cannot help in unraveling the mystery. You are our last hope. Fly right away in the direction of nebula ACD-1587."

The next day I got my old photon rocket back from the repair shop and installed in it my time accelerator and my electronic robot who knows all the languages of the cosmos and all the stories about interstellar travel (it is guaranteed to keep me entertained for at least a five year journey). Then I took off to attend to the matter at hand.

Just as the robot exhausted his entire supply of stories and had begun to repeat himself (nothing is worse than listening to an electronic robot repeating an old story for the tenth time), the goal of my journey appeared in the distance. The galaxies which covered up the mysterious line lay behind me, and in front of me was ... the hotel Cosmos. Some time ago I constructed a small planet for wandering interstellar exiles, but they tore this apart and again were without a refuge. After that, they decided to give up wandering into foreign galaxies and to put up a grandiose building—a hotel for all travelers in the cosmos. This hotel extended across almost all the galaxies. I say "almost all" because the exiles dismantled a few uninhabited galaxies and made off with a few poorly situated constellations from each of the remaining ones.

But they did a marvelous job of building the hotel. In each room there were faucets from which hot and cold plasma flowed. If you wished, you could be split into atoms for the night, and in the morning the porter would put your atoms back together again.

But, most important of all, there was an *infinite number of rooms* in the hotel. The exiles hoped that from now on no one would have to hear that irksome phrase that had plagued them during their time of wandering: "no room available."

In spite of this I had no luck. The first thing that caught my eye when I entered the vestibule of the hotel was a sign: Delegates to the cosmic zoologists' congress are to register on the 127th floor.

Since cosmic zoologists came from all the galaxies and there are an infinite number of these, it turned out that all the rooms were occupied by participants in the conference. There was no place for me. The manager tried, it is true, to get some of the delegates to agree to double up so that I could share a room with one of them. But when I found out that one proposed roommate breathed fluorine and another considered it normal to have the temperature of his environment at about 860°, I politely turned down such "pleasant" neighbors.

Luckily the director of the hotel had been an exile and well remembered the good turn I had done him and his fellows. He would try to find me a place at the hotel. After all, you could catch pneumonia spending the night in interstellar space. After some meditation, he turned to the manager and said:

"Put him in number 1."

"Where am I going to put the guest in number 1?"

"Put him in number 2. Shift the guest in number 2 to number 3, number 3 to number 4, and so on."

It was only at this point that I began to appreciate the unusual qualities of the hotel. If there had been only a finite number of rooms, the guest in the last room would have had to move out into interstellar space. But because the hotel had infinitely many rooms, there was space for all, and I was able to move in without depriving any of the cosmic zoologists of his room.

The following morning, I was not astonished to find that I was asked to move into number 1,000,000. It was simply that some cosmic zoologists had arrived belatedly from galaxy VSK-3472, and they had to find room for another 999,999 guests. But while I was going to the manager to pay for my room on the third day of my stay at the hotel, I was dismayed to see that from the manager's window there extended a line whose end disappeared somewhere near the clouds of Magellan. Just then I heard a voice:

"I will exchange two stamps from the Andromeda nebula for a stamp from Sirius."
"Who has the stamp Erpean from the 57th year of the cosmic era?"

I turned in bewilderment to the manager and asked:

"Who are these people?"
"This is the interstellar congress of philatelists."
"Are there many of them?"
"An infinite set—one representative from each galaxy."
"But how will you find room for them; after all, the cosmic zoologists don't leave till tomorrow?"

"I don't know; I am on my way now to speak to the director about it for a few minutes."

However, this time the problem turned out to be much more difficult and the few minutes extended into an hour. Finally, the manager left the office of the director and proceeded to make his arrangements. First he asked the guest in number 1 to move to number 2. This seemed strange to me, since I knew from my own experience that such a shift would only free one room, whereas he had to find places for nothing less than an infinite set of philatelists. But the manager continued to give orders:

"Put the guest from number 2 into number 4, the one from number 3 into number 6; in general, put the guest from number n into number $2n$."

Now his plan became clear: by this scheme he would free the infinite set of odd-numbered rooms and would be able to settle the philatelists in them. So in the end the even numbers turned out to be occupied by cosmic zoologists and the odd numbers by philatelists. (I didn't say anything about myself—after three days of acquaintance I became so friendly with the cosmic zoologists that I had been chosen an honorary representative to their congress; so I had to abandon my own room along with all the cosmic zoologists and move from number 1,000,000 to number 2,000,000). And a philatelist friend of mine who was 574th in line got room number 1147. In general, the philatelist who was nth in line got room number $2n - 1$.

The following day the room situation eased up—the cosmic zoologists' congress ended and they took off for home. I moved in with the director, in whose apartment there was a vacant room. But what is good for the guests does not always please the management. After a few days my generous host became sad.

"What's the trouble?" I asked him.
"Half the rooms are empty. We won't fulfill the financial plan."

Actually, I was not quite sure what financial plan he was talking about; after all, he was getting the fee for an infinite number of rooms, but I nevertheless gave him some advice:

"Well, why don't you move the guests closer together; move them around so as to fill all the rooms."

This turned out to be easy to do. The philatelists occupied only the odd rooms: 1, 3, 5, 7, 9, etc. They left the guest in number 1 alone. They moved number 3 into number 2, number 5 into number 3, number 7 into number 4, etc. At the end all the rooms were once again filled and not even one new guest had arrived.

But this did not end the director's unhappiness. It was explained that the exiles did not content themselves with the erection of the hotel Cosmos. The indefatigable builders then went on to construct an infinite set of hotels, each of which had infinitely many rooms. To do this they dismantled so many galaxies that the intergalactic equilibrium was upset and this could entail serious consequences. They were therefore asked to close all the hotels except ours and put the material used back into place. But it was difficult to carry out this order when all the hotels (ours included) were filled. He was asked to move all the guests from infinitely many hotels, each of which had infinitely many guests, into one hotel, and this one was already filled!

"I've had enough!" the director shouted. "First I put up one guest in an already full hotel, then another 999,999, then even an infinite set of guests; and now they want me to find room in it for an additional infinite set of infinite sets of guests. No, the hotel isn't made of rubber; let them put them where they want."

But an order was an order, and they had five days to get ready for the arrival of the new guests. Nobody worked in the hotel during these five days—everybody was pondering how to solve the problem. A contest was announced—the prize would be a tour of one of the galaxies. But all the solutions proposed were turned down as unsuccessful. Then a cook in training made the following proposal: leave the guest in number 1 in his present quarters, move number 2 into number 1001, number 3 into number 2001, etc. After this, put the guest from the second hotel into numbers 2, 1002, 2002, etc. of our hotel, the guests from the third hotel into numbers 3, 1003, 2003, etc. The project was turned down, for it was not clear where the guest of the 1001st hotel were to be placed; after all, the guests from the first 1000 hotels would occupy all the rooms. We recalled on this occasion that when the servile Roman senate offered to rename the month of September "Tiberius" to honor the emperor (the preceding months had already been given the names of Julius and Augustus), Tiberius asked them causticly "and what will you offer the thirteenth Caesar?"

The hotel's bookkeeper proposed a pretty good variant. He advised us to make use of the properties of the geometric progression and resettle the guests as follows: the guests from the first hotel are to be put in rooms 2, 4, 8, 16, 32, etc. (these numbers form a geometric progression with multiplier 2). The guests from the second hotel are to be put in rooms

3, 9, 27, 81, etc. (these are the terms of the geometric progression with multiplier 3). He proposed that we resettle the guests from the other hotels in a similar manner. But the director asked him:

"And we are to use the progression with multiplier 4 for the third hotel?"

"Of course," the bookkeeper replied.

"Then nothing is accomplished; after all, we already have someone from the first hotel in room 4, so where are we going to put the people from the third hotel?"

My turn to speak came; it was not for nothing that they made you study mathematics for five years at the Stellar Academy.

"Use prime numbers. Put the guests from the first hotel into numbers 2, 4, 8, 16, ..., from the second hotel into numbers 3, 9, 27, 81, ..., from the third into numbers 5, 25, 125, 625,..., the fourth into numbers 7, 49, 343,...."

"And it won't happen again that some room will have two guests?" the director asked.

"No. After all, if you take two prime numbers, none of their positive integer powers can equal one another. If p and q are prime numbers, $p \neq q$, and m and n are natural numbers, then $p^m \neq q^n$."

The director agreed with me and immediately found an improvement on the method I had proposed, in which only the primes 2 and 3 were needed. Namely, he proposed to put the guest from the mth room of the nth hotel into room number $2^m 3^n$. This works because if $m \neq p$ or $n \neq q$, $2^m 3^n \neq 2^p 3^q$. So no room would have two occupants.

This proposal delighted everyone. It was a solution of the problem that everyone had supposed insoluble. But neither the director nor I got the prize; too many rooms would be left unoccupied if our solutions were adopted (according to mine—such rooms as 6, 10, 12, and, more generally, all rooms whose numbers were not powers of primes, and according to the director's—all rooms whose numbers could not be written in the form $2^n 3^m$). The best solution was proposed by one of the philatelists, the president of the Academy of Mathematics of the galaxy Swan.

He proposed that we construct a tabulation, in whose rows the number of the hotel would appear, and in whose columns the room numbers would appear. For example, at the intersection of the 4th row and the 6th column there would appear the 6th room of the 4th hotel. Here is the tabulation (actually, only its upper left part, for to write down the entire tabulation we would have to employ infinitely many rows and columns):

$$
\begin{array}{ccccccc}
(1,1) & (1,2) & (1,3) & (1,4) & (1,5) & \ldots & (1,n) & \ldots \\
(2,1) & (2,2) & (2,3) & (2,4) & (2,5) & \ldots & (2,n) & \ldots \\
(3,1) & (3,2) & (3,3) & (3,4) & (3,5) & \ldots & (3,n) & \ldots \\
(4,1) & (4,2) & (4,3) & (4,4) & (4,5) & \ldots & (4,n) & \ldots \quad (1.1) \\
(5,1) & (5,2) & (5,3) & (5,4) & (5,5) & \ldots & (5,n) & \ldots \\
 & & & & \vdots & & \vdots & \\
(m,1) & (m,2) & (m,3) & (m,4) & (m,5) & \ldots & (m,n) & \ldots \\
 & & & & \vdots & & \vdots &
\end{array}
$$

"And now settle the guests according to squares," the mathematician-philatelist said.

"How?" The director did not understand.

"By squares. In number 1 put the guest from $(1,1)$, i.e., from the first room of the first hotel; in number 2 put the guest from (1, 2), i.e., from the second room of the first hotel; in number 3 put the guest from (2, 2), the second room of the second hotel, and in number 4—the guest from (2, 1), the first room of the second hotel. We will thus have settled the guests from the upper left square of side 2. After this, put the guest from (1, 3) in number 5, from (2, 3) in number 6, from (3, 3) in number 7, from (3, 2) in number 8, from (3, 1) in number 9. (These rooms fill the square of side 3.) And we carry on in this way:

$$
\begin{array}{cccccccc}
(1,1) & (1,2) & (1,3) & (1,4) & (1,5) & \ldots & (1,n) & \ldots \\
& \downarrow & \downarrow & \downarrow & \downarrow & & \downarrow & \\
(2,1) \leftarrow & (2,2) & (2,3) & (2,4) & (2,5) & \ldots & (2,n) & \ldots \\
& & \downarrow & \downarrow & \downarrow & & \downarrow & \\
(3,1) \leftarrow & (3,2) \leftarrow & (3,3) & (3,4) & (3,5) & \ldots & (3,n) & \ldots \\
& & & \downarrow & \downarrow & & \downarrow & \\
(4,1) \leftarrow & (4,2) \leftarrow & (4,3) \leftarrow & (4,4) & (4,5) & \ldots & (4,n) & \ldots \\
& & & & \downarrow & & \downarrow & \\
(5,1) \leftarrow & (5,2) \leftarrow & (5,3) \leftarrow & (5,4) \leftarrow & (5,5) & \ldots & (5,n) & \ldots \\
& & & & & & \downarrow & \\
(n,1) \leftarrow & (n,2) \leftarrow & (n,3) \leftarrow & (n,4) \leftarrow & (n,5) \leftarrow & \ldots & (n,n) & \ldots
\end{array}
$$

$$(1.2)$$

"Will there really be enough room for all?" The director was doubtful.

"Of course. After all, according to this scheme we settle the guests from the first n rooms of the first n hotels in the first n^2 rooms. So sooner or later every guest will get a room. For example, if we are talking about the guest from number 136 in hotel number 217, he will get a room at the 217th stage. We can even easily figure out which room. It will have the number $216^2 + 136$. More generally, if the guest occupies room n in the mth hotel, then if $n \geq m$ he will occupy number $(n-1)^2 + m$, and if $n < m$, number $m^2 - n + 1$."

The proposed project was recognized to be the best—all the guests from all hotels would find a place in our hotel, and not even one room would be empty. The mathematician-philatelist received the prize—a tour of galaxy LCR-287.

In honor of this so successful solution, the director organized a reception to which he invited all the guests. The reception, too, had its problems. The occupants of the even-numbered rooms arrived a half hour late, and when they appeared, it turned out that all the chairs were occupied, even though our kind host had arranged to have a chair for each guest. They had to wait while everyone shifted to new places so as to free the necessary quantity of seats (of course, not one new chair was brought into the hall). Later on when they began to serve ice cream to the guests, it was discovered that each guest had two portions, although, as a matter of fact, the cook had only prepared one portion per guest. I hope that by now the reader can figure out by himself how this happened.

At the end of the reception I got into my photon rocket and took off for Earth. I had to inform the cosmonauts of Earth about the new haven existing in the cosmos. Besides, I wanted to consult some of the prominent mathematicians and my friend Professor Tarantog about the properties of infinite sets.

From the Author

With this we take leave temporarily of our hero. Many of his stories give rise to doubt—after all, according to the laws of the theory of relativity it is impossible to transmit signals at speeds greater than 186,000 miles/sec. Thus, even the very first order of the director would require infinitely many intervals of time to carry out. But let us not ask too much of Ion the Quiet—he has had even more improbable adventures during his travels.

The rest of the book is devoted to the story of the theory of sets. And although the events will no longer take place in interstellar space but on the interval [0, 1] or the square of side 1, many of them will seem no less unusual.

2

Sets and Operations on Sets

What Do We Mean by a Set?

Before we can discuss the properties of infinite sets, we have to become acquainted with the meaning of the term *set* and the kind of operations that can be carried out on sets. Unfortunately, we are not in a position to give a rigorous definition of the fundamental concept of the theory: the concept of set. Of course, we could say that a set is a *collection*, a *union*, an *ensemble*, a *family*, a *system*, a *class*, etc. But this would not be a mathematical definition, but rather a misuse of the multitude of words available in the English language.

In order to define a concept we have to indicate first of all that it is a special case of a more general concept. This is impossible for the concept of set, since this concept is already as broad as possible and is thus not a special case of any other concept.

So, instead of giving a definition of the concept of set, we shall simply illustrate its nature by means of examples.

It is frequently necessary to speak of various objects which share some general property. For example, we might talk about the set of chairs in a room, about the set of all atoms in Jupiter, about the set of all cells in the human body, about the set of all potatoes in a particular sack, about the set of all fish in the ocean, about the set of all squares in the plane, about the set of all points on a given circle, etc.

The objects which compose the given set are called its *elements*. In order to indicate that a given set A consists of elements x we usually write

$$A = \{x\} \qquad (2.1)$$

Here the braces mean that the elements x are united into a new whole—the set A. We represent the statement that element x belongs to set A with the aid of the symbol as follows: $x \in A$. If the element x does not belong to set A, then we write $x \notin A$. For instance, if A denotes the set of all even natural numbers, then $6 \in A$, while $3 \notin A$.

Thus, when we speak of a set, we unite many objects into a new entity; namely, into the set which consists of these elements. The founder of the theory of sets, Georg Cantor, stressed this in the following words:

The set is a multitude conceived of by us as a one.

In order to gain insight into the notion of set, the academician N. N. Luzin proposed the following way of representing it. Imagine a transparent, impenetrable shell, something like a tightly closed, transparent sack. We suppose that all the elements of a given set A are contained within this shell, and that no other objects are present within the shell except these. This same transparent shell enclosing all the elements (and nothing besides them) is a rather good representation of the act of uniting all the elements x, the result of which is to construct the set A.

If the set contains a finite number of elements, we call the set *finite*, and if the set contains infinitely many elements, we call the set *infinite*. For example, the set of trees in the forest is finite, while the set of points on a circle is infinite.

How We Specify a Set

Of course, there are various ways of specifying a set. One way is to give a complete list of the elements composing a set. For instance, the set of pupils in a given class is determined by the list in the class register, the set of all countries on the globe is listed in any atlas, the set of all bones in the human skeleton is listed in textbooks of anatomy.

But we can only apply this method to finite sets, and certainly not even to all of them. As an example, take the set of fishes in the sea; it is finite, but it is hardly possible to give a list of all of them. We could not even begin

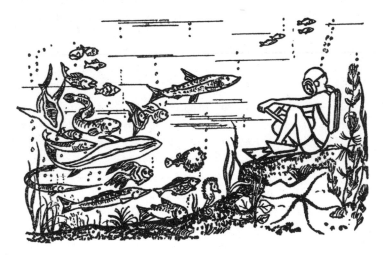

Fig. 3.   The great census of the fishes.

to define an infinite set with the aid of a list; for example, try to make a list of all the natural numbers—it is clear that the construction of this list could never be completed.

In those cases in which the set cannot be specified by means of a list, we determine it by making use of some characteristic property that is possessed by all elements of the set, but which no other objects possess. We might, for example, speak of the set of all natural numbers. It is then clear that the number **73** belongs to this set, while the

Fig. 4. The crocodile does not belong to the set of natural numbers.

number 3/4 or a crocodile does not belong. In exactly the same way neither $\sqrt{2}$ nor the planet Saturn belongs to the set of all rational numbers, while **7/15** does belong to this set.

In practice, let us note, the determination of sets by means of characterizing criteria runs into difficulty because of the ambiguity of our language. The task of separating the objects belonging to a set from those that do not is often made difficult by the large number of objects of intermediate type. Suppose, for example, that we are talking about the set of all trees on our globe. First of all, we must decide whether we mean all the trees which existed or will exist, or whether we mean the trees which existed during the course

of a fixed interval of time (perhaps from the 1st of May to
the 1st of September 1967). But how about the trees that
were cut down during this period of time? Moreover, there
exists a whole series of intermediate forms separating trees
from other types of plants, so that we have to decide which
of these are to belong to the set and which are not.

Similarly, when we discuss the set of all lines of poetry
published in the year 1967, we are confronted with the
existence of numerous forms of writing intermediate between
poetry and prose (rhythmical prose, blank verse, etc). It is
not too difficult to define the set of people who enjoy the
right of free travel on the railroads of the Soviet Union.
In particular, in this set we have all children less than 5
years old. But it might happen that one of our youthful
passengers has his fifth birthday in the course of the trip, so
that it becomes unclear whether or not he belongs to the set
(let us say that one punctilious father uses a stop watch
to determine exactly the remaining portion of the journey
for which he is to pay, starting from the moment his son
becomes five years old).

Subtle points like this crop up even in simpler cases.
Suppose, for example, that the set A consists of all the
letters of the first line of the famous story *Eugene Onegin*.
This definition can be understood in two ways. On the one
hand, we could be talking about the set composed of all the
letters in this line; then each letter occurs in the set as many
times as it occurs in the line (in order to distinguish the
letters from one another we can use numerical indices);

$$\text{М}_1, \text{О}_1, \text{Й}_1, \text{Д}_1, \text{Я}_1, \text{Д}_2, \text{Я}_2, \text{С}_1, \text{А}_1, \text{М}_2,$$

$$\text{Ы}_1, \text{Х}_1, \text{Ч}_1, \text{Е}_1, \text{С}_2, \text{Т}_1, \text{Н}_1, \text{Ы}_2, \text{Х}_2, \text{П}_1,$$

$$\text{Р}_1, \text{А}_2, \text{В}_1, \text{И}_1, \text{Л}_1 \tag{2.2}$$

But we could also suppose that we were talking about the set of distinct letters of the Russian alphabet which occurred in this line. In this case we would drop any repetitions of a letter, so that the set would consist of the following letters:

$$\text{М, О, Й, Д, Я, С, А, Ы, Х, Ч, Е, Т, Н, П, Р, В, И, Л} \quad (2.3)$$

It is clear that (2.2) and (2.3) are two distinct sets.

To Shave or Not to Shave?

Not all the difficulties connected with the determination of a set relate to inadequacies of language. Sometimes the cause lies deeper. As a rule, the set itself is not one of its elements (for example, the set of all natural numbers is not a natural number, the set of all triangles is not a triangle, etc). In general, however, the nature of the elements of a set is quite arbitrary, and no one can prohibit us from discussing sets which contain themselves as elements. Since such sets are discussed only rarely, we shall call them *exceptional* sets, while the remaining sets shall be called *ordinary* sets.

We can now describe the set A consisting of *all* ordinary sets. At first glance, there does not appear to be anything wrong with this definition; it is not obvious why the phrase "set of all ordinary sets" is any more wrong than the phrase "set of all triangles." But here we run into a serious logical contradiction, indeed. Let us try to make clear why this same set A is both ordinary and exceptional. If it is ordinary, then it occurs as one of its own elements (after all, we have collected together all ordinary sets). But then by definition it must be exceptional. If the set A is exceptional, then, by definition of exceptional set, it must be one of its own elements, but all the elements of A are ordinary sets; so we didn't take an exceptional set after all.

We have obtained an insoluble logical contradiction: the set A can neither be ordinary nor exceptional. Moreover, such logical contradictions arise in even simpler cases. A

Fig. 5. To shave or not to shave?

soldier was ordered to shave those soldiers and only those soldiers of his platoon who did not shave themselves. The question arose of whether he should shave himself. If he shaved himself, then he would be among the group of soldiers who shaved themselves, but he doesn't have the right to shave those soldiers. If he doesn't shave himself, then he belongs to the class of soldiers who do not shave themselves, but then according to the order he has been given he must shave himself.

There are other well-known examples of sets which at first glance appear to be well defined, but turn out on closer inspection to be very poorly defined, and we would be better off saying that these sets are not defined at all. For example, let A be the set of real numbers which can be defined with the aid of at most two hundred English words (here we include the words "zero," "one," "two," etc).

Since the set of all English words is finite (for simplicity we may assume that we only choose words found in Webster's dictionary and their grammatical derivatives), the set of all such real numbers is finite. But this means that the set can be enumerated. Let us suppose that this enumeration has already been carried out, and let us define the number N in the following way. This number has the form

$$N = 0, n_1 n_2 n_3 \ldots n_k \ldots \qquad (2.4)$$

Here we look at the kth digit occurring in the kth word in our list of the set A and agree to set $n_k = 1$, if this digit is distinct from 1. If the kth digit of the kth number is 1, then we put $n_k = 2$.

Thus, N is not equal to the kth number of set A, since it differs from it at the kth place. Since k was arbitrary, it follows that N cannot equal any number of set A and so does not belong to this set. However, N has to belong to the set A, because we used less than two hundred words in its definition.

This paradox is closely related to the following one:

What is the smallest integer that cannot be defined by means of a sentence having less than two hundred English words?

Such a number exists since the number of words in the English language is finite; so that there must be a number that cannot be defined by means of a sentence having less than two hundred words. And, of course, among these numbers there would have to be a smallest.

On the other hand, this number cannot exist, since its definition involves a contradiction. Indeed, this number is defined by the sentence written above in italics, which we see contains less than two hundred words; while according to its definition this number cannot be determined by such a sentence.

Many examples occur in the theory of sets in which the definition of the set is self-contradictory. The study of the question of the conditions under which this takes place leads to deep questions of logic. Consideration of these questions has completely changed the face of the subject. Many of these studies were subsequently used in constructing the theory of electronic computers, in the theory of automata, etc. Since these investigations belong rather to the subject of mathematical logic, we shall not touch on them here.

We shall only be concerned with sets which are well defined and defined in such a way that there is no question at this point (such as the set of all natural numbers, the set of all squares in the plane and so on).

The Empty Set

The very name "set" leads us to think that any set must contain many elements (at least two). But this is not the case. In mathematics it is sometimes necessary to examine sets having only one element and sometimes even a set having no elements at all. This set is called the *empty set* and is denoted by the symbol $\varnothing$.

Why should we be interested in an empty set?

First of all, let us take note of the fact that when a set is determined by means of some characteristic property, it is not always known in advance whether there are any elements with this property. For instance, let the set A consist of all quadrilaterals such that

(a) all of their angles are right angles,
(b) the diagonals have different lengths.

If someone does not know geometry, he will not see anything contradictory in these requirements. However, it follows from the theorem on the equality of the diagonals of a rectangle that the set of all such quadrilaterals is empty. The same is true of the set of all triangles the sum of whose angles is different from $180°$. The set of quadratic polynomials having more than two roots is likewise empty. More generally, many mathematical statements can be formulated so as to become statements about the emptiness of a certain set (try to formulate the theorem of Pythagoras in this way).

There are also sets nonmathematical in nature that are empty: the set of all people whose age is more than 300 years, the set of all carp who live on land, the set of all planets of the solar system rotating about the star Sirius.

There are also some sets about which we do not know whether they are empty or not. For example, it is unknown at present whether the set of all natural numbers n such that $n > 2$ and n satisfies the equation

$$x^n + y^n = z^n \qquad (2.5)$$

is empty or not (this is the famous problem of Fermat). It is also not known whether the set of digits occurring at most a finite number of times in the decimal expansion of π is finite or not (although the decimal expansion of π has been carried out to several thousands of digits, it is still unknown whether all digits occur in its decimal expansion an infinite number of times or whether some digit only occurs in it a finite number of times).

We also don't know if the set of all living plesiosaurs on earth is empty—if the Loch Ness monster really turns out to be a plesiosaur, then this set is not empty.

The Theory of Sets and Elementary Mathematics

A set can be composed of quite varied elements: fish, houses, squares, numbers, points, etc. Indeed, this explains the extraordinary breadth of the theory of sets and its applicability to the most varied branches of knowledge (mathematics, mechanics, physics, biology, linguistics, etc.). For mathematics, of course, the sets composed of "mathematical objects" play an especially important role; among these mathematical objects are geometric figures, algebraic equations, functions, etc. Some of these sets are involved in elementary mathematics, but the word "set" is usually lacking there (this is explained simply if we recall that the most "modern" part of elementary mathematics came into being at the end of the 17th century, while the theory of sets is a child of the 19th century).

Indeed, in elementary mathematics we encounter sets at every turn. Sets of numbers, i.e., sets composed of numbers, are met with especially frequently. As examples of such sets we can take:

(a)   the set of all natural numbers,
(b)   the set of all integers (positive, negative, and zero),
(c)   the set of all rational numbers,
(d)   the set of all real numbers,
(e)   the set of all complex numbers.

Two kinds of sets turn up in geometry. First of all, in geometry we ordinarily talk about the properties of some set of geometric figures. For example, the theorem stating that the diagonals of a parallelogram bisect each other relates to the set of all parallelograms. Secondly, the geometric figures are themselves sets composed of the points occurring within them. We can therefore speak of the set of all points contained within a given circle, of the set of all points within a given cone, etc.

In algebra we meet such sets as the set of all polynomials in two variables, the set of all quadratic equations, the set of all roots of a given equation, etc. In other words, almost every part of elementary mathematics is connected with the theory of sets in some way or other.

Subsets

The concept of set turns out to be very useful in mathematics. This is due to the fact that the elements of a set can be of the most varied nature. The same statement in terms of sets can be interpreted as a statement concerning points of a geometric figure, as a statement concerning natural numbers, as a statement concerning animals or plants, and as a statement concerning atoms and molecules. The concepts and theorems of the theory of sets have wide generality. We shall now discuss some of them. We need first to become acquainted with the notion of *subset*. This notion comes up each time we have to consider a set not only in itself but as a part of another, larger set. In fact, we say that set B is a subset of set A, if each element x in B is also an element of A. Here we write $B \subset A$.

For example, if we pick some high school, the set of sophomores is a subset of the set of all students in the school.

In turn, the set of students in this school is a subset of the set of all students.

In geometry too, we frequently have to deal with subsets of some set of geometric figures. Consider, for example, the following sets:

(a)   Set A consists of all quadrilaterals;
(b)   set B consists of all trapezoids;
(c)   set C consists of all parallelograms;
(d)   set D consists of all rectangles;
(e)   set E consists of all squares.

In this list each figure is a special case of the figure of the preceding type (the trapezoid is a special type of quadrilateral, the parallelogram is a special type of trapezoid, etc). But this means that each set is a subset of its predecessor:

$$A \supset B \supset C \supset D \supset E \qquad (2.6)$$

Similarly, each set in the following list is a subset of its predecessor.

(a)   The set of all complex numbers,
(b)   the set of all real numbers,
(c)   the set of all rational numbers,
(d)   the set of all integers,
(e)   the set of all natural numbers.

In many cases, in order to single out a subset from a given set it is sufficient to specialize the characterizing property of the set in some way or to give some supplementary condition. For example, the subset of natural numbers can be obtained from the set of integers by adding on the condition $n > 0$.

The Universal Set

Very rarely we might happen to be carrying out a discussion in which both the set of all complex numbers and the set of all whales in the ocean occurred (of course, we cannot exclude the possibility that the theory of functions of a complex variable might be applicable to the study of the motion of whales in water). More commonly, we find that all the sets involved in a discussion are subsets of some fixed set I. In this case we call the set I the *universal set*.

For example, in arithmetic the universal set is the set of all nonnegative rational numbers, in algebra it is the set of complex numbers and algebraic functions, in mathematical analysis it is the set of real functions of a real variable, and in geometry it is the set of all points in Euclidean space. Any geometric figure is, of course, a subset of the set of all points of Euclidean space.

The Intersection of Sets

In applications of mathematics we often have to deal with those elements of a collection of sets which occur in each set of the collection. These elements form a new set called the *intersection* of the given sets or their (*set*) *product*. And this operation of forming a new set is called *taking the intersection* or *multiplying* the sets in question. Thus, *taking the intersection of some sets A, B, C, . . . results in a new set containing just those elements which occur in each of the sets A, B, C, ...*

The name "intersection" derives from the fact that when we take the intersection of the sets of points in two geometric figures, we obtain the intersection of the two figures in the ordinary sense of the word. In Fig. 6 we show a line intersecting a circle in the chord AB. The set of points on this segment is the intersection of the set of points of the line with the set of points of the circle.

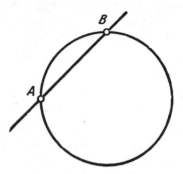

FIG. 6.   A line intersecting a circle in the chord AB.

But the concept of intersection is not only applicable to geometric figures. For example, suppose that the students of a given school participate in four kinds of sport: football, swimming, chess, and boxing. The intersection of the sets of participants in each sport will consist of those all-round athletes who play football, swim, box, and know the chess openings.

We sometimes have to take the intersection of sets of geometric figures or numbers. For instance, the set of all squares is the intersection of the set of all rectangles with the set of all rhombuses. The set of all right triangles is the intersection of all triangles with the set of all polygons containing right angles. The intersection of the set of all natural numbers divisible by 2 with the set of all natural numbers divisible by 3 is the set of all natural numbers divisible by 6.

The intersection of two sets A and B is usually denoted by either AB or $A \cap B$. The operation of taking the intersection possesses properties reminiscent of those possessed by the operation of multiplying numbers. Namely, it satisfies the commutative and associative laws

$$AB = BA \tag{2.7}$$

and

$$A(BC) = (AB)C \tag{2.8}$$

The empty set plays a role in the intersection (multiplication) of sets similar to the role played by zero in multiplication of numbers. In fact, for any set A we have the equality

$$AO = O \tag{2.9}$$

analogous to the equality $a \cdot 0 = 0$.

The universal set plays a role analogous to that of unity: for any subset A of I we have the equality

$$AI = A \tag{2.10}$$

analogous to the equality $a \cdot 1 = a$.

However, there are properties of set multiplication which arc not analogous to properties of numerical multiplication. For example, if B is a subset of A, $B \subset A$, then we have the equality $BA = B$. For in this case all the elements of B (and just those elements) are simultaneously in both A and B.

In particular, for any set A we have the equality

$$AA = A \tag{2.11}$$

Union of Sets

We now study the union of sets, which amounts to forming a new whole out of several sets. The *union* (or sum) of sets A, B,... is a new set consisting of just those elements that occur in at least one of the sets in question. The union of two sets A and B is usually denoted by $A + B$ or $A \cup B$.

We have to bear in mind that some of the elements may occur in more than one of the sets in question. In spite of this, they still occur only once in the union. Thus, if the sets involved are finite, it may turn out that the number of elements in the union is less than the sum of the numbers of elements in the individual sets. For example, let the first set be the set of all letters of the Russian alphabet occurring in the first line of "Eugene Onegin," and the second consist of the letters occurring in the second line of this poem. We have already written down the first set. It consists of the 18 letters

$$\text{М, О, Й, Д, Я, С, А, Ы, Х, Ч, Е, Т, Н, П, Р, В, И, Л} \quad (2.3)$$

The second set consists of the 13 letters:

$$\text{К, О, Г, Д, А, Н, Е, В, Ш, У, Т, З, М} \quad (2.12)$$

The union of these two sets is the following collection of 23 letters:

$$\text{М, О, Й, Д, Я, С, А, Ы, Х, Ч, Е, Т, Н, П, Р,}$$
$$\text{В, И, Л, К, Г, Ш, У, З} \quad (2.13)$$

The letters О, Д, А, Н, Е, В, Т, М, occurring in the intersection of these two sets occur only once in the union, so that we obtain only 23 letters rather than $18 + 13 = 31$ letters.

Here is yet another example in which the individual sets have elements in common. The set of all students in the class is the union of the following three sets:

(a) the set of passing students,
(b) the set of girls in the class,
(c) the set of boys who are not passing.

It is clear that every student of the class belongs to at least one of these three sets. However, these sets have common elements: the girls who are passing are in both the first and the second sets.

Sometimes the union is taken over an infinite collection of sets. For example, let A_n denote the set of all positive fractions with denominator n:

$$A_1 = \left\{\frac{m}{1}\right\}, \quad A_2 = \left\{\frac{m}{2}\right\}, \quad \ldots, \quad A_n = \left\{\frac{m}{n}\right\}, \quad \ldots \quad (2.14)$$

The union of all the sets $A_1, A_2, \ldots, A_n, \ldots$ is the set of all positive fractions, i.e., all the fractions of the type m/n, where m and n are natural numbers.

Let A_3 denote the set of all right triangles, let A_4 denote the set of right quadrilaterals, let A_5 denote the set of right five sided figures, etc. Then the union of all these sets is the set A of all right polygons.

Set unions also occur in algebra. If A is the set of roots of the equation

$$f(x) = 0 \qquad (2.15)$$

and B is the set of roots of the equation

$$\varphi(x) = 0 \qquad (2.16)$$

then the set of roots of the equation

$$f(x)\varphi(x) = 0 \qquad (2.17)$$

is $A + B$ (here we do not take the multiplicity of a root into account).

The operation of taking the union of sets has many properties analogous to those of the addition of numbers. Thus, we have the commutative and associative laws:

$$A + B = B + A \qquad (2.18)$$

and

$$A + (B + C) = (A + B) + C \qquad (2.19)$$

The empty set again plays the role of zero in the union of sets: no matter what set A is chosen, we always have the equality

$$A + O = A \qquad (2.20)$$

But the role of the universal set is no longer the role of unity in the addition of numbers. For any set A we have

$$A + I = I \qquad (2.21)$$

In general, if B is a subset of A, then $B + A = A$. In particular, for any set A we have $A + A = A$.

The operations of addition and multiplication of sets obey the distributive law

$$A(B + C) = AB + AC \qquad (2.22)$$

In order to show that this law is obeyed we have to show that each element on the left-hand side of the equality is present on the right-hand side, and conversely.

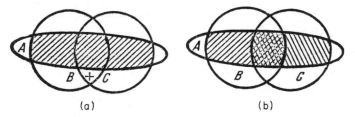

(a) (b)

Fig. 7a, b.   Illustration of equality (2.22).

It is not difficult to carry out a rigorous proof of this law, but the details are somewhat tedious. For this reason we shall simply present two figures which illustrate equality (2.22). The shaded region in Fig. 7a is the intersection of set A with the set $B + C$; in Fig. 7b we show the intersection of A with B and A with C. It is quite obvious from these pictures that equality (2.22) holds. Moreover, for sets there is another "distributive law" which does not hold for numbers. It is expressed in the formula

$$A + BC = (A + B)(A + C) \qquad (2.23)$$

It can be proved simply by expanding the right-hand side according to formula (2.22) and taking note of the fact that AB and AC are both subsets of A; thus, $AC \subset A$ and $AB \subset A$. In addition, $AA = A$, so that

$$AA + AC + BA + BC = A + BC \qquad (2.24)$$

Partitioning of Sets

Considered in general, the summands occurring in a union of sets may have elements in common. However, we sometimes encounter a set which is the union of its own subsets, no two of which have elements in common (or, as we would usually say, no two intersect). In this case we say that set A has a *decomposition into disjoint subsets*.

Decompositions into subsets frequently arise in the classification of objects. For example, when a catalog of the books in a library is being compiled, they are first divided into works of fiction, books of political and social science, books on the natural sciences, etc. After this, each of the subsets obtained is further subdivided into smaller subsets: works of fiction are divided into prose and poetry, books on the social and political sciences are divided into books on philosophy, political economy, etc., books on the natural sciences are divided into books on mathematics, physics, etc. This subdivision makes it convenient to find any desired book.

Of course, the same set can be decomposed into disjoint subsets in different ways. When, in that same library, they compile the alphabetic index, they first divide the books into the subset of books whose authors' names begin with A, the subset of books whose authors' names begin with B, etc. After this each of the subsets is again subdivided in correspondence with the second letter of an authors' name, etc.

The concept of *equivalence* of elements is frequently used in the decomposition of sets. We first have to define what is meant by the phrase "element x is equivalent to element y," and we can then unite all equivalent elements in one subset. However, not just any notion of equivalence will do for a decomposition. For example, we could say that two people are equivalent if they know one another. But it can happen that person X knows person Y, that person Y knows person Z, while person X and person Z are not acquainted. Then we have to put people X and Y in the same subset (they know one another), after that Z must also be included (he knows Y), so we find that in our subset we have people that are not acquainted: X and Z. In order to avoid this undesirable situation it is necessary that the notion of equivalence satisfy the following three conditions:

(a)   each element is equivalent to itself;
(b)   if element x is equivalent to element y, then element y is equivalent to element x;
(c)   if element x is equivalent to element y and element y is equivalent to element z, then element x is equivalent to element z.

It can be proved that the fulfillment of these three conditions is necessary and sufficient for a decomposition of A into subsets of mutually equivalent elements to exist (moreover, distinct subsets have no elements in common).

For example, we might say that two integers x and y are equivalent if their difference is an even integer. It is easy to verify that this definition of equivalence satisfies all three conditions (a)–(c). By gathering all mutually equivalent integers into a subset we effect a partition of the set of all integers into two subsets: the set of even integers and the set of odd integers.

Subtraction of Sets

When there is a notion of sum, a notion of difference can usually be found. Sets are not an exception to this rule. The difference of sets A and B will be a new set $A - B$, in which there occur all those elements of set A which do not belong to set B. Here we need make no requirement about B being a subset of A. If B is not a subset of A, then the subtraction of B from A reduces to the removal from A of the common part of A and B:

$$A - B = A - AB \qquad (2.25)$$

For example, if A is the set of points contained in the first circle appearing in Fig. 8 and B is the set of points

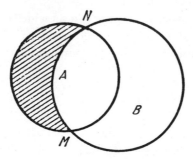

FIG. 8.

contained in the second circle, then their difference is the set of points contained in the shaded crescent-shaped figure (minus the arc MN). If A is the set of all students of a given class in some school and B is the set of all girls attending this school, then $A - B$ is the set of all boys who are students in the class in question.

In case B is a subset of A, we say that $A - B$ is the *complement* of set B relative to A and denote it by $B_{A'}$ (of course, the same set B will have different complements relative to different sets A containing it). For example, the complement of the set of even numbers relative to the set of all integers is the set of all odd numbers. The complement of the set of all squares in the set of all rectangles is the set of all rectangles with unequal adjacent sides. On the other hand, the complement of this same set of squares in the set of all rhombuses is the set of rhombuses with unequal diagonals.

If all the sets under consideration are subsets of a universal set I, then by the complement of the set B we usually understand its complement relative to I. In this case we write B' instead of $B_{I'}$.

Due to the fact that elements occurring in several of the summands only occur once in the union of the summands, and since it is possible to subtract a set which is not contained in the minuend, several of the formulas of arithmetic cease to hold for subtraction of sets. It may happen, for instance, that

$$(A + B) - C \neq A + (B - C) \tag{2.26}$$

Indeed, if all three sets coincide, $A = B = C$, then the left hand side is the empty set, while the right-hand side is equal to A.

The Algebra of Sets

We have become acquainted with operations on sets as well as with some properties of these operations. In addition to these properties we might have discussed a whole series of others. We shall now present a list of all the general properties of the set-theoretical operations introduced (in this list O will denote the empty set, I will denote the universal set, A' will denote the complement of set A with respect to the universal set):

[1]　$A \subset A$.

[2]　If $A \subset B$ and $B \subset A$, then $A = B$.

[3]　If $A \subset B$ and $B \subset C$, then $A \subset C$.

[4]　$O \subset A$.

[5]　$A \subset I$.

[6]　$A + B = B + A$.

[7]　$AB = BA$.

[8]　$A + (B + C) = (A + B) + C$.

[9]　$A(BC) = (AB)C$.

[10]　$A + A = A$.

[11]　$AA = A$.

[12]　$A(B + C) = AB + AC$.

[13]　$A + BC = (A + B)(A + C)$.

[14]　$A + O = A$.

[15]　$AI = A$.

[16]　$A + I = I$.

[17]　$AO = O$.

[18]　The relation $A \subset B$ is equivalent to either of the relations $A + B = B$, $AB = A$.

[19]　$A + A' = I$.

[20]　$AA' = O$.

[21]　$O' = I$.

[22]　$I' = O$.

[23]　$(A')' = A$.

[24]　The relation $A \subset B$ is equivalent to the relation $B' \subset A'$.

[25] $(A + B)' = A'B'$.
[26] $(AB)' = A' + B'$.

Using properties [1–26], we can carry out operations on sets in exactly the same way as we carry out operations on numbers in ordinary algebra. In fact, certain formulas have an even simpler form than in ordinary algebra. For example, the binomial formula reduces to the following simple equality:

$$(A + B)^n = A + B \qquad (2.27)$$

as may be readily checked by use of property [11].

We shall not prove properties [1–26]; they can be checked by use of pictures (Venn diagrams) just as we checked property [12]. The proof of properties [25] and [26] is a little more complicated than that of the others.

Of course, it is not an easy task to commit properties [1–26] to memory. But this is not at all necessary; indeed, it is enough to become acquainted with the two fundamental operations: addition of sets and the taking of complements. The latter two operations must satisfy the following three relations:

$$A + B = B + A \qquad (2.28)$$

$$(A + B) + C = A + (B + C) \qquad (2.29)$$

$$(A' + B')' + (A' + B)' = A \qquad (2.30)$$

We can now define the operation of multiplication AB and the containment relation $A \subset B$ by means of the formulas

$$AB = (A' + B')' \qquad \text{(by definition)} \qquad (2.31)$$

$$A \subset B \quad \text{means} \quad A + B = B \qquad (2.32)$$

Then all the properties [1–26] will follow from formulas (2.28)–(2.32).

We point out the following remarkable "duality relation." If in each of the properties [1–26] we interchange the symbols

$$\subset \quad \text{and} \quad \supset$$

$$0 \quad \text{and} \quad I$$

$$+ \quad \text{and} \quad \cdot$$

then in each case the result of the interchange is again one of the above properties. For example, if we apply this procedure to property [6], property [7] results; if we apply it to property [12], property [13] results, etc.

It follows from this that whenever a theorem can be proved by use of properties [1–26], then its corresponding "dual theorem," obtained by interchanging the indicated symbols, is also true.

Boolean Algebras

In addition to sets, we encounter other objects in mathematics for which operations of addition and multiplication possessing properties [1–26] are defined. Such collections of objects were first studied in 1847 by the English mathematician Boole. Such systems are therefore called *Boolean algebras*.

An interesting example of a Boolean algebra is formed by the set of all divisors of the number 30: $M = \{1, 2, 3, 5, 6, 10, 15, 30\}$. Here the operation of "addition" is to be the formation of the least common multiple, while that of "multiplication" is to be the formation of the greatest common divisor. For example, $2 \oplus 5 = 10$, $6 \odot 15 = 3$ (we have enclosed the symbols of addition and multiplication in circles in order to distinguish them from the usual addition and multiplication of numbers). The relation

$a \subset b$ means that a is a divisor of the number b. The role of the element O is played by the number 1, while the number 30 plays the role of the element I. As the complement of the divisor a we must take the number $a' = 30/a$. For example, $10' = 3$.

Of course, it is not necessary to verify that all of the properties [1–26] hold; as we mentioned above, it is sufficient to verify that properties (2.28)–(2.32) are satisfied for this system.

3

The Cardinality of Sets

Equality between Sets

Up till now we have been concerned with properties of sets which held generally for both finite and infinite sets. Here we shall be interested in properties characteristic of infinite sets alone. We have already seen in the story of Ion the Quiet that these properties are quite different from those of finite sets—things impossible for finite sets turn out to be possible for infinite sets.

The first question which we shall now discuss is the problem of deciding when two infinite sets are equal to one another. For finite sets of the most varied types we can always say which of them contains the larger number of elements. This problem is much more complicated for infinite sets. For example, which is the larger set, that of the natural numbers or that of the rational numbers, that of the rational numbers or that of the real numbers? Are there more points on the entire line than there are on a segment, more points in a square than on a line?

It appears quite simple at first glance to answer these questions. After all, the set of natural numbers is only a part of the set of rational numbers and the segment is only a part of the line. Isn't it obvious, therefore, that there are fewer natural numbers than there are rational numbers and that there are fewer points on a segment than in a square? It turns out not to be so obvious. It does not follow at all that when we go from finite to infinite sets, the laws derived from the study of the former remain valid; for example, a law such as "the part is less than the whole."

Above all, an attempt to base equality for infinite sets on the criterion that one is a part of the other is doomed to failure in advance. For example, where are there more points, in a square or on the whole of an infinite line? After all, the square cannot be contained in a line and, without breaking it, it is impossible to put a line inside a square. Of course, it is possible to break the line up into segments of length equal to the side of the square, and after that place each segment inside the square in such a way that no two intersect. But how do we know that we can find a way to break up the square so that the parts can be strung out along the line without overlapping? And how many infinite sets there are which are not parts of one another! The set of squares in the plane and the set of circles in the same plane do not have even a single element in common. How can we compare them? How can we find out if there are more atoms of nitrogen or of oxygen in the universe?

We have now posed the problem. First we investigate under what conditions it can be said that one set contains just as many elements as another. In other words, we study the conditions under which two infinite sets have "the same measure" of elements.

On the Dance Floor

The problem of comparison is easily solved for finite sets. In order to find out if the number of elements is the same for two sets, we have only to count them. If we get the same numbers, this means that both sets have the same size. But such a procedure is not suitable for infinite sets; for, having begun to count the elements of an infinite set, we run the risk of devoting our entire lives to this job and still not completing the enterprise we have undertaken.

And the method of counting is not always convenient even for finite sets. For instance, let us go to a dance hall. How can we tell if the numbers of boys and girls here are the same? Of course, we could ask the boys to go off to one side and the girls to the other, and undertake to count both groups. But, in the first place, this would give us superfluous information; we are not interested in how many boys and girls are here, but only in whether the numbers are the same. And then, the young people on the dance floor did not get together to stand around and wait for the end of the count, but to dance.

Well, what then? Let us satisfy their wish and ask the orchestra to play a dance that everybody knows how to do. Then the boys will ask the girls to dance and ... our problem will be solved. After all, if it turns out that all the boys and girls are dancing, i.e., if all the young people are paired off, then it is obvious that there are just as many boys as girls on the dance floor.

We could find out by an identical procedure whether the number of spectators in a theater is equal to the number of seats. If during the performance all the places are taken, no spectator is standing in the aisles and one spectator is sitting in each seat, then we can be sure that there are just as many spectators as seats.

When people are running down the street in rainy weather, the number of people is the same as the number of raincoats; for each person wears only one raincoat and no one would risk running along the street without a raincoat.

For Every Flow There Is an Ebb

We have seen how it is possible to determine that two finite sets have equally many elements without having recourse to counting. We can also apply this method to infinite sets. But here we can no longer get an orchestra to do the job; we ourselves have to distribute the elements of the two sets to be compared into "couples."

Then suppose we are given two sets A and B. We shall say that we have established a *one-to-one correspondence* between them, if the elements of these sets have been joined in pairs (a, b) such that:

(1) element a belongs to set A, and element b belongs to set B;
(2) every element of the two sets occurs in one and only one pair.

For instance, if set A consists of the boys on the dance floor and set B consists of the girls found there, then pair (a, b) is composed of the boy and girl dancing together. If set A consists of the spectators and set B consists of the seats in the theater, then pair (a, b) is composed of the spectator and the seat in which he sits. Finally, if A is the set of people on the street and B is the set of their raincoats, then pair (a, b) is composed of the person and his raincoat.

Naturally, not every correspondence between sets is one-to-one. If set A consists of all the trees in the world and set B consists of all the fruit growing on these trees, then we can set up the following correspondence between these sets: to each fruit we make correspond the tree on which it grows. But this is not a one-to-one correspondence: many pieces of fruit grow on some trees, while other trees do not even bear fruit. Thus, some elements *a* (trees) will appear in many pairs, while other elements *a* will not appear in any.

It means the same thing for two finite sets to say that there is a one-to-one correspondence between them, or to say that they have equally many elements. The fundamental turning point in the theory of sets came when Cantor decided to compare infinite sets in the same manner.

In other words, Cantor said that two (possibly infinite) sets *A* and *B* have equally many elements, if it is possible to set up a one-to-one correspondence between them.

Mathematicians do not usually say: "sets *A* and *B* have equally many elements"; they say: "*A* and *B* have the same *cardinality*" or they say: "sets *A* and *B* are *equivalent*."

Because of this, the word *cardinality* means the same thing for infinite sets as the words "number of elements" do for finite sets.

The Czech savant B. Bolzano arrived at the notion of one-to-one correspondence independently of Cantor; but he gave up the further pursuit of the idea because of the difficulties into which it led him. As we shall soon see, we shall have to set aside many cherished habits of thought once we accept the principle of comparing infinite sets with the aid of the one-to-one correspondence.

Can a Part Be Equal to the Whole?

One dogma that we have to brush aside is the statement, established at the beginning of the development of mathematics: *a part is less than the whole*. This statement is indisputably true for finite sets, but it loses its force when we try to apply it for infinite sets. Let us recall how the director of the extraordinary hotel shifted the cosmic zoologists to even-numbered rooms. He moved the inhabitant of room n to room $2n$. In other words, he moved them according to the following scheme:

$$
\begin{array}{ccccc}
1 & 2 & 3 & \ldots & n & \ldots \\
\downarrow & \downarrow & \downarrow & & \downarrow & \\
2 & 4 & 6 & \ldots & 2n & \ldots
\end{array}
\tag{3.1}
$$

But this scheme sets up a one-to-one correspondence between the set of natural numbers

$$1, 2, 3, \ldots, n, \ldots \tag{3.2}$$

and a part of this set: the set of even numbers

$$2, 4, 6, \ldots, 2n, \ldots \tag{3.2a}$$

But we agreed to assume that two sets contain equally many elements if it is possible to set up a one-to-one correspondence between them. This means that the set of natural numbers contains as many and only as many elements as one of its subsets, the set of even numbers.

In exactly the same way we could set up a one-to-one correspondence between the set of natural numbers and the set of numbers of the form

$$10, 100, 1000, 10\,000, \ldots \tag{3.3}$$

To do this we need only associate the natural number n with the number 10^n:

$$n \to 10^n \tag{3.4}$$

This establishes the desired one-to-one correspondence. In the same way we can set up a one-to-one correspondence between the set of all natural numbers and the set of all squares of natural numbers:

$$n \to n^2 \tag{3.5}$$

the set of all cubes of natural numbers:

$$n \rightarrow n^3 \tag{3.6}$$

and so on.

Generally speaking, we can set up a one-to-one correspondence between the set of all natural numbers and any of its infinite subsets. To do this we need only write down the numbers of this subset in a sequence.

Countable Sets

We call sets having equally many elements as the set of natural numbers *countable sets*. In other words, a set is called countable if it is infinite and its elements can be counted with the aid of the natural numbers. For example, the set of even numbers, the set of odd numbers, the set of primes, and, in general, any infinite subset of the natural numbers are countable sets.

We sometimes have to employ considerable ingenuity in order to show that this or that set is countable. Let us take as our example the set of all integers (both positive and negative):

$$\ldots, -n, \ldots, -3, -2, -1, 0, 1, 2, 3, \ldots, n, \ldots \tag{3.7}$$

If we try to number them beginning at some given place, we find that the numbering is incomplete; for all the numbers occurring before the given place have not been counted. In order not to leave out any numbers we have to write the set in two lines:

$$\begin{array}{ccccccc} 0, & 1, & 2, & 3, & 4, & 5, & 6, \ldots \\ -1, & -2, & -3, & -4, & -5, & -6, & -7, \ldots \end{array} \tag{3.8}$$

and number by columns. Here 0 is assigned the number 1, -1 is assigned the number 2, 1 the number 3, -2 the number 4, etc. In other words, zero and all the positive integers are numbered with odd numbers, while all the negative integers are numbered with even numbers. This resembles the way the hotel director placed the philatelists in a hotel already filled with cosmic zoologists.

But if it is easy to show that the set of integers is countable, it is more difficult to show that the same is true of the rational numbers. After all, the rationals are densely distributed: between any two rational numbers we can still find infinitely many rational numbers. So it is quite unclear how we should go about numbering them; it would seem that between any two numbers we would still have to number an infinite set, so that the process would never end. And it really is impossible to write down the rationals in a sequence in which each number is greater than its predecessor.

But if we do not concern ourselves about the magnitude of the numbers in our sequence, we can succeed in numbering them. Let us first write down all positive fractions with denominator 1, then all positive fractions with denominator 2, then with denominator 3, and so on. We get a tabulation like the following:

$$\frac{1}{1}, \quad \frac{2}{1}, \quad \frac{3}{1}, \quad \frac{4}{1}, \quad \frac{5}{1}, \ldots$$

$$\frac{1}{2}, \quad \frac{2}{2}, \quad \frac{3}{2}, \quad \frac{4}{2}, \quad \frac{5}{2}, \ldots$$

$$\frac{1}{3}, \quad \frac{2}{3}, \quad \frac{3}{3}, \quad \frac{4}{3}, \quad \frac{5}{3}, \ldots \tag{3.9}$$

$$\frac{1}{4}, \quad \frac{2}{4}, \quad \frac{3}{4}, \quad \frac{4}{4}, \quad \frac{5}{4}, \ldots$$

$$\frac{1}{5}, \quad \frac{2}{5}, \quad \frac{3}{5}, \quad \frac{4}{5}, \quad \frac{5}{5}, \ldots$$

$$\ldots\ldots\ldots\ldots\ldots\ldots\ldots\ldots\ldots$$

Clearly, every positive rational number will appear in this table, and more than once. For example, the number 3 occurs in the form of the fractions 3/1, 6/2, and 9/3.

Now we commence with the numbering. For this we recall the last exploit of the director of the extraordinary hotel, the one in which he found places for the guests of infinitely many such hotels. In doing this he numbered by squares. We shall proceed in the same manner, but with this complication: we shall leave out some of the fractions (for example, since 1/1 is assigned number 1, we drop the fractions 2/2, 3/3, etc, for they express the same number). We get the following enumeration of the positive rationals: 1, 2, 1/2, 3, 3/2, 2/3, 1/3, 4, 4/3, 3/4, 1/4,.... .

Thus we can number all the positive rationals. It is now easy to explain how all the rational numbers (both positive and negative) can be numbered. We separate them into two tables, using even numbers to number one table and odd numbers for the other (remembering to reserve a number for zero).

In general, if we take the union of a countable set of countable sets, we again get a countable set. We could prove this by using this same technique of numbering by squares.

Algebraic Numbers

All the examples we have given up to this point are actually special cases of a general theorem. This comes about because in all of these examples the elements of the sets can be specified by means of a finite collection of natural numbers. For example, any integer n (except zero) can be written in the form

$$(-1)^k |n| \tag{3.10}$$

where $|n|$ is the absolute value of the number, and k is 1, if $n < 0$, and 2, if $n > 0$. Thus the integer n is determined by means of a pair of natural numbers $(k, |n|)$. In the same way we can write any positive rational number in the form of an irreducible fraction m/n, or, what is the same thing, we can employ the pair of natural numbers (m, n).

The general theorem to which we referred reads as follows:

Theorem 3.1. *If every element in a set can be specified by means of a finite collection of natural numbers, then this set is finite or countable.*

The basic idea of the proof of Theorem 3.1 is quite similar to one of the methods employed by the director of the hotel in solving his most difficult problem; the details, however, are more complicated.

We start off by taking all the primes 2, 3, 5, 7, 11, 13, etc, writing them $p_1, p_2, \ldots, p_n, \ldots$. If the element x of A is specified by the collection of natural numbers $\{m_1, \ldots, m_n\}$, then we let it correspond to the natural number

$$N_x = p_1{}^{m_1} \ldots p_n{}^{m_n} \qquad (3.11)$$

It follows from the theorem asserting the uniqueness of the decomposition of natural numbers into products of primes that different elements of A correspond to different natural numbers. Thus, the mapping $x \to N_x$ sets up a one-to-one correspondence between the elements of set A and a subset of the natural numbers.

We shall prove later that any infinite subset of the natural numbers is countable, so that by combining this fact with the result of the previous paragraph we see that set A is either finite or countable.

With the help of this theorem we can prove, for example, that the set of all algebraic numbers is countable.

Algebraic numbers are roots of algebraic equations with integer coefficients $a_0, \ldots, a_n$:

$$a_0 x^n + a_1 x^{n-1} + \ldots + a_n = 0 \qquad (3.12)$$

For example, $\sqrt[4]{5}$ is an algebraic number, for it is a root of the equation

$$x^4 - 5 = 0 \qquad (3.13)$$

Numbers that are not algebraic are called *transcendental*.

Each equation of nth degree has exactly n roots. Thus, any algebraic number is determined by a collection of integers:

$$\{k, a_0, a_1, \ldots, a_n\} \qquad (3.14)$$

where $a_0, \ldots, a_n$ are the coefficients of Eq. (3.12) and k is the index of the root. The numbers $a_0, \ldots, a_n$ can assume any integral values, while k is a natural number between 1 and n. If we now apply Theorem 3.1, we see that the set of all algebraic integers is countable.*

Unequal Sets

We have already explained what we mean when we say: "two sets have equally many elements." Now we are going to explain what we mean when we say: "one set has more elements than another." For finite sets this too can be found out without resorting to counting. Recall our example involving the dance floor.

---

* The requirement that the numbers $a_0, \ldots, a_n$ be integers rather than natural numbers does not raise any problems, for the integers can be enumerated.

If, after the orchestra starts playing and the boys have invited the girls to dance, there are some boys leaning against the wall, then it is clear that there are more boys. On the other hand, if we see some girls sadly watching their friends dancing, it is clear that there are more girls.

FIG. 9.   An atom from each fish.

In these examples we proceeded as follows: we tried to establish a one-to-one correspondence between one set, the first, and part of another set, the second. If this worked out, then the second set had more elements than the first. By employing this method we could prove, for example, that there are fewer fish in the ocean than atoms on the Earth (although both these sets are finite, it is hardly possible to count them). We can do this by simply letting each fish correspond to one of the atoms constituting its body. This sets up a one-to-one correspondence between the set of all fish and part of the set of all atoms on Earth.

FIG. 10a.

FIG. 10b.
No partner for him.

Unfortunately, this simple procedure fails to hold good for infinite sets. Indeed, we recently saw that a set can have equally many elements as one of its parts. So we are in no position to conclude from the sole fact that A has as many elements as a part of set B, that set A has fewer elements than set B.

We shall be more modest in our demands and say that if we can set up a one-to-one correspondence between set A and part of set B, then set B has *no fewer elements than set A.* We could prove that this relation possesses all the fundamental properties of inequalities:

(1) Each set *A* has no fewer elements than itself.
(2) If set *A* has no fewer elements than set *B*, and *B* has no fewer elements than set *C*, then *A* has no fewer elements than *C*.
(3) If *A* has no fewer elements than *B*, and *B* has no fewer elements than *A*, then they have equally many elements (that is, we can set up a one-to-one correspondence between the elements of these sets).

It can happen that set *B* has no fewer elements than set *A*, but these sets are not equivalent. In other words, there could exist a one-to-one correspondence between set *A* and part B_1 of set *B* without there existing a one-to-one correspondence between *A* and all of set *B*. This is the case in which we shall say that *B* has more elements than *A*.

The Countable Set—The Smallest of the Infinite Sets

We already said that any infinite subset of the set of natural numbers is countable. This means that there can be no infinite set whose cardinality is less than the cardinality of a countable set. Let us now prove that any infinite set contains a countable subset. We can conclude from this that the cardinality of a countable set is not greater than the cardinality of any infinite set, i.e., that this cardinality is the smallest infinite cardinality.

We can select a countable subset from the infinite set *A* in the following way: Take any element *x*—we can do this because the set *A* is infinite, and so is certainly not empty. Clearly, we have not exhausted the elements of *A* with the selection of element *x*, so that we can proceed to select a second element x_1. After that, we choose a third element x_2, etc. We have thus extracted from set A a countable subset X of indexed elements:

$$X = \{x_1, x_2, \ldots, x_n, \ldots\} \tag{3.15}$$

By making a slight change in the argument we can arrange matters so that an infinite set will be left even after the extraction of the countable subset. All we have to do is put back into A all those elements from X that have even indices. After doing this, we have extracted a countable subset

$$Y = \{x_1, x_3, x_5, \ldots\} \tag{3.16}$$

and the remaining part of the set still contains an infinite subset of elements: $\{x_2, x_4, x_6, \ldots, x_{2n}, \ldots\}$ (and possibly other elements).

It is not difficult to prove the following theorems.

Theorem 3.2. *The cardinality of an infinite set is not changed when we adjoin a countable set to it.*

Theorem 3.3. *The cardinality of an uncountable set is not changed when we extract a countable subset from it.*

Theorems **3.2** and **3.3** again assert that the countable set is the smallest of the infinite sets.

Uncountable Sets

All the sets we have constructed so far have been countable. This naturally leads us to ask whether all infinite sets are countable. If so, the mathematician would have an easy life: all infinite sets would have equally many elements and no further analysis of infinity would be necessary. But the situation turns out to be more complicated than that; uncountable sets exist, and of more than one cardinality. We are already acquainted with one uncountable set—the set of all points on a straight line. But rather than speak of this set, we are going to discuss a set closely related to it, the set A of ways in which the rooms of the extraordinary hotel can be occupied.

Note that it is usually not easy to prove that a set is uncountable. After all, to prove that a set is countable means simply to invent a method of enumerating its elements. But to prove that a set is uncountable we have to prove that no such method exists. In other words, no matter what method we applied, some element of the set would fail to be counted. Cantor conceived of a very clever method for proving the uncountability of sets which is called the diagonal process (actually, we encountered it on p. 23). Cantor's method of proof is made clear by the following story about Ion the Quiet.

The Census That Never Took Place

Up to now I have talked about the successes of the director of the extraordinary hotel: about how he managed to find places for an infinite set of new guests in his already full hotel, and how he later was able to find places even for the guests from infinitely many such unusual hotels. But there was a time when even this wizard met failure.

An order came down from the commissioner of cosmic hotels to compile a list as quickly as possible of all the possible ways in which the rooms of the hotel could be occupied. The list was to be presented in the form of a table, each line of which was to reflect one of the various ways of occupying

the hotel. The filled rooms were to be indicated by ones
and the empty rooms by zeros. For example, the sequence

$$101010101010\ldots \tag{3.17}$$

meant that all the odd rooms were filled and all the even
rooms were empty. The sequence

$$11111111111\ldots \tag{3.18}$$

meant that the entire hotel was filled, while the sequence

$$000000000000\ldots \tag{3.19}$$

indicated a financial catastrophe—all the rooms were empty.

The director was overloaded with work and therefore
conceived of a simple way out of the situation. He charged the
man on duty on each floor to compose a list of the ways in
which just the rooms in his charge could be occupied. No two
ways on the list were to be the same. After a few days the
lists were presented to the director and he combined them all
into one list.

"Are you sure that this list is complete?" I asked the
director. "Isn't there some other way of occupying the
rooms?"

"I don't know" he replied. "There are infinitely many
ways listed and I don't know how to test the list for
completeness."

At this point an idea flashed into my head (by the way,
I may be overestimating my talents, because not all traces
of my discussions with Professor Tarantog on infinite sets
had vanished from my mind).

"I can guarantee that the list is incomplete. I can select
a way that is sure to be lacking."

"I agree that the list is probably incomplete. But you won't succeed in selecting a way that isn't listed; after all, there are already infinitely many listed."

We made a bet. I proposed to win it by nailing each sequence on the door of the room to which it corresponded (the reader will recall that there were just as many ways listed as rooms in the hotel). I then proceeded in a very simple fashion. Going up to the door of the first room, I saw that the corresponding sequence started with the digit 0. The digit 1 quickly appeared on my writing pad; this was the first digit of the sequence I wanted to construct.

When I went up to the door of the second room, I wasn't interested in the first digit of that sequence; after all, I already had the first digit of my sequence. So I directed my attention to the second digit. Seeing that this was 1, I wrote the digit 0 on my pad. Similarly, when I noticed that the third digit of the sequence nailed to the first room was also 1, I again wrote the digit 0 on my pad. In general, when I found that the nth digit of the nth sequence was 0, then I wrote the digit 1 in the nth place on my pad, but if the nth digit of the nth sequence was 1, then I wrote 0.

After I had gone past all the rooms of the hotel,* a sequence of zeros and ones had been written on my pad.

Going to the director's office, I said:

"Here, feast your eyes on the missing sequence."
"And how do you know that it's lacking?"
"It can't be the first because it has a different first digit. It can't be the second because it has a different second digit; in general, it can't be the nth because it has a different nth digit."

---

* Hm, how much time did he have to spend?

The bet was won, and I gained the privilege to stay at the hotel whenever I wanted at no charge.

But it at once became clear that no matter what countable set of sequences you took, there would always be a sequence that didn't appear in the list (you would always be able to hang them on the doors of the rooms). This means that the set of all ways of occupying the hotel is uncountable, and the task given the director was not one that could be carried out.

We decided to send a telegram describing the situation. I should point out that the telegraph in use at the extraordinary hotel was itself unusual: it could send telegrams composed of an infinite set (more precisely, a countable set) of dots and dashes. For example, the telegram might have the form

$$— \cdot — — \cdot — — — \cdot \quad \text{etc} \qquad (3.20)$$

I quickly grasped the fact that the set of all such telegrams was also uncountable; after all, you could just as well put zeros and ones in place of the dots and dashes, and then there would be no difference at all between the telegrams with a countable set of signs and the set of all ways of occupying the hotel.

After sending the telegram, I took leave of the director of the hotel and took off for galaxy RGC-8067, where I was to carry out an astrographical survey.

The Uncountability of the Continuum

Now it will not be difficult to prove that the set of all points on a line is uncountable. In place of it we can discuss the set of all real numbers, since to each point on the line there corresponds a real number, and conversely.

Any real number can be given an infinite decimal expansion of the form

$$a . \alpha_1 \alpha_2 \alpha_3 \ldots \alpha_n \ldots \qquad (3.21)$$

Some even have two expansions, for example: 0.500000... and 0.49999999... both represent the same number. To simplify matters we shall employ the expansion with the zeros.

Suppose that by some scheme we had managed to enumerate all the real numbers. In order to show that this can't happen we need only show that some number has not been enumerated. Following in Ion the Quiet's footsteps, we proceed in the following manner.

We first write zero followed by a decimal point. We then take the first number in our enumeration and examine its first place after the decimal point (i.e., its tenths place). If it differs from 1, then we write a 1 after the decimal point in the number we are constructing; but if it is 1, we put a 2 after the decimal point. After that we choose the second number in our enumeration and examine its second place after the decimal point. Again, if this number is different from one, we put the number 1 in the hundredths place in our number; and if it is 1, then we use 2. We carry on in this way, each time looking at the nth place in the nth number of our enumeration. As a result of these operations we get some number, for example:

$$N = 0.1121211 \ldots \qquad (3.22)$$

It is clear that this number is not one of those enumerated: it differs from the first number in the first decimal place; it differs from the second number in the second decimal place; it differs from the nth number in the nth decimal place, etc. (compare p. 60).

In order to make it clearer to the reader how we determine our number different from all those enumerated, suppose that in the given enumeration the first five numbers have the following form:

$$4.27364\ldots$$
$$-1.31226\ldots$$
$$7.95471\ldots \qquad (3.23)$$
$$0.62419\ldots$$
$$8.56280\ldots$$

Then the number not in the enumeration will begin with the following decimals:

$$0.12121\ldots \qquad (3.24)$$

Naturally, this is not the only number that is not on the list (we could have replaced all the decimals except 2 by 2 and replaced 2 by 7, or chosen some other rule). But we only needed to establish the existence of one single number which does not appear in the enumeration in order to demonstrate that the supposed enumeration of all the real numbers could not exist.

The Existence of Transcendental Numbers

Numbers are called *transcendental numbers* if they are not the roots of any equation with integer coefficients of the form

$$a_0 x^n + a_1 x^{n-1} + \ldots + a_n = 0 \qquad (3.25)$$

The numbers which are roots of such equations are called *algebraic numbers*.

During a long period in its history mathematics only dealt with algebraic numbers, such as $7/15$, $\sqrt[8]{10}$, $\sqrt{2} + \sqrt[3]{3}$, etc. It was only at the cost of a great effort that the French mathematician Liouville was able to find a few transcendental numbers in 1844. But the proof that the number π was transcendental, carried out by Lindemann in 1882, was a great mathematical event; indeed, it followed as a consequence that it was impossible to square the circle. And suddenly it became clear that the algebraic numbers met with at every step in mathematics are really extremely rare, while the transcendental numbers, so hard to construct, were really the common ones. After all, we have already seen that the algebraic numbers only form a countable set; while the set of all real numbers, as we only just demonstrated, is uncountable. This means that the difference between the real numbers and the algebraic numbers, i.e., the transcendental numbers, must also be uncountable.

The proof that transcendental numbers exist, carried out by G. Cantor in 1873, greatly impressed the mathematical world. Indeed, Cantor was able to demonstrate the existence of transcendental numbers without the need of constructing a single concrete example, using only general arguments. But the virtue of Cantor's proof was at the same time its weakness. It was impossible to deduce a rule from Cantor's reasoning which would allow the construction of even a single transcendental number, to say nothing of a test for the transcendence of such numbers as π or $2^{\sqrt{2}}$. His arguments constituted, as mathematicians say, a pure existence proof.

Long and Short Line Segments Have Equally Many Points

Unless the reader had been acquainted with the remarkable properties of infinite sets, the question "Are there more points on a line segment 1 foot long or on a line segment 1 mile long?" would hardly have raised a shadow of doubt in his mind. The answer was clear; there are many more points on the segment of length 1 mile, for isn't it 5280 times longer? But by now, probably, the reader has learned to beware of making categorical statements—the properties of infinite sets are too dissimilar to what he has been taught to expect by daily life.

And the long and short segments do in fact have equally many points! In other words, it is possible to set up a one-to-one correspondence between the points of these segments. Figure 11 represents the easiest way of showing how this can be done.

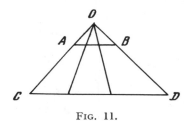

Fig. 11.

It is hard to reconcile oneself to the thought that a path a million light years long has only as many points as the radius of an atomic nucleus!

But even more unexpected is the result that there are not even more points on the entire infinite line than on the segment, i.e., a one-to-one correspondence can be set up between the set of points on the line and the set of points on the segment.

We do not even need the whole segment, but can discard its endpoints (i.e., we use the open interval). It is clear from Fig. 12 how to set up a one-to-one correspondence between the interval and the line. It is clear that each point

on the interval corresponds to exactly one point on the line
and that every point on the line has a mate on the interval.

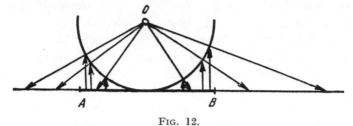

Fig. 12.

However, this correspondence can be set up in another
way with the help of a curve—the tangent curve, the graph
of the function $y = \tan x$ (Fig. 13).

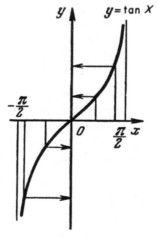

Fig. 13.

Segment and Square

Mathematicians reluctantly reconciled themselves with
the fact that there are as many points on a segment as on an

infinite line. But the following result of Cantor turned out to be even more unexpected. Searching for a set which would have more points than a segment, he turned to the set of points of a square. He had no doubt of the result— after all, the segment occupied in all only one side of the square, whereas the set of all segments which composed the square had the cardinality of the continuum.

Cantor searched for three years (from 1871 to 1874) for a proof that it was impossible to set up a one-to-one correspondence between the points of the segment and the points of the square.

The years went by, but the desired result could not be obtained. And then the completely unexpected happened. He succeeded in setting up the correspondence he believed impossible! He wrote to the mathematician Dedekind: "I see it, but I don't believe it."

But we have to resign ourselves to the fact that our intuition lets us down again here—it turns out that there are exactly as many points in the square as on the segment. A rigorous proof of the statement is made somewhat complicated by the lack of uniqueness of the decimal expansion of numbers. We shall therefore present only a sketch of Cantor's proof.

Let us take the segment $[0, 1]$ and the square of side 1. We may suppose that the square is situated as in Fig. 14. We have to set up a one-to-one correspondence between the points of the segment and the points of the square. Projection of the points of the square onto the segment AB will not help here; indeed, under projection an infinite set of points of the square are sent into one point of the segment (for example, all the points of segment DA go into point A).

We can solve the problem as follows: We can specify any point T of the square $ABCD$ by means of two numbers, its coordinates x and y (or more simply its distances along the sides AB and AD). These numbers can be written as

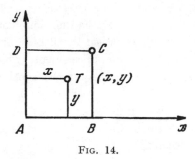

FIG. 14.

infinite decimals. Since x and y are not more than 1, these decimals have the form

$$x = 0. \alpha_1 \alpha_2 \ldots \alpha_n \ldots \tag{3.26}$$

$$y = 0. \beta_1 \beta_2 \ldots \beta_n \ldots \tag{3.27}$$

(for the sake of simplicity we do not take points lying on the sides of the square, but only take interior points). Here are the decimals of the numbers x and y, for example, if $x = 0.63205\ldots$ and $y = 0.21357\ldots$, then $\alpha_1 = 6$, $\alpha_2 = 3$, $\alpha_3 = 2$, etc, and $\beta_1 = 2$, $\beta_2 = 1$, $\beta_3 = 3$, etc.

Now we have to pick the point Q of the segment AB which is to correspond to T. It is enough to say what the length of the segment AQ is. We choose this length to be equal to the number z, whose decimal expansion is obtained by "shuffling" the decimal expansions of x and y. In other words, we form a third expansion from the two expansions (3.26) and (3.27) by combining their decimals.

$$z = 0. \alpha_1 \beta_1 \alpha_2 \beta_2 \alpha_3 \beta_3 \ldots \alpha_n \beta_n \ldots \tag{3.28}$$

For instance, if

$$x = 0.515623\ldots \tag{3.29}$$

and

$$y = 0.734856\ldots \tag{3.30}$$

then we obtain

$$z = 0.571354682536\ldots \tag{3.31}$$

The point 2 lies on the segment [0, 1], and it is clear that different points of the square correspond to different points of the segment. Indeed, if points T and T' are not the same, then the decimal expansion of x and x' or y and y' must differ at least in one place. But this will lead to a difference in the decimal expansions of the numbers z and z'. A somewhat more detailed analysis shows that the corresponding points also do not coincide.

Thus we have set up a one-to-one correspondence between the points of the square and the points of a part of the segment [0, 1]. This shows that the set of points of the square has a cardinality no larger than that of the set of points of the segment. But its cardinality is certainly no smaller, so that the cardinalities must coincide.

Not just the square, but the cube as well has only as many points as the segment. In general, any geometric figure containing at least one line segment will have just as many points as the segment. Such sets are called sets with the cardinality of the *continuum* (from the Latin *continuum*—unbroken).

Somehow One Problem Does Not Work Out

We have now been acquainted for a while with two kinds of infinite sets. One kind has just as many elements as the set of natural numbers, and the other kind has just as many as the set of points of the line. We determined that there were more elements in the second set. It is now natural to ask ourselves the question: "Isn't there some set 'in between' which has more elements than the set of natural numbers and fewer elements than the set of points on the line?" This question has been given the name of the *continuum problem*. Many distinguished mathematicians have pondered it, starting with Georg Cantor himself, but the problem remained unsolved up to very recent times.

Academician N. N. Luzin, one of the most prominent mathematicians and the founder of the Soviet school of real variable theory, meditated on the continuum problem during the course of many years. But the solution was as elusive as a mirage in the desert (true, in the course of his reflections on this problem N. N. Luzin solved a whole series of the most difficult problems of set theory and founded a separate branch of mathematics—the descriptive theory of sets).

One day a fifteen-year-old boy Lev Shniselman was brought in to N. N. Luzin. He was said to possess exceptional mathematical ability (later on he became one of the most prominent Soviet mathematicians and a corresponding member of the Academy of Sciences of the USSR). In order to test the capabilities of this young mathematician N. N. Luzin proposed that he solve thirty extremely difficult problems. He was able to do 29 of the problems, but one was... the continuum problem. Alas, at the end of a month the young mathematician came back to N. N. Luzin and sadly told him: "Somehow one problem doesn't work out."

The failure of the attempts to solve the continuum problem was not accidental. The situation here is reminiscent of the history of the parallel postulate. For two thousand years attempts were made to deduce this axiom from the remaining axioms of geometry. It became clear after the work of Lobachevsky, Hilbert, and other mathematicians that it did not contradict the other axioms, but could not be derived from them. Similarly, it became clear after the work of K. Gödel, P. S. Novikov, P. J. Cohen, and others that the assertion that there is no set of intermediate cardinality does not contradict the other axioms of set theory, but also cannot be derived from these axioms.

Is There a Set of Largest Cardinality?

Till now the largest cardinality we have become acquainted with is that of the set of points on the line, i.e., the cardinality of the continuum. Neither the set of points of the square nor the set of points of the cube has a larger cardinality. Perhaps the cardinality of the continuum is the largest possible? This turns out not to be the case. Indeed, there is no set of largest cardinality. Given any set A, there is a set of cardinality greater than the cardinality of A. We can construct it by associating to each point a of a set A the function $f^a(x)$ assuming the value 1 at this point and the value 0 at the remaining points. Clearly, distinct points give rise to distinct functions. For example, if set A consists of the points 1, 2, 3, then point 1 corresponds to a function which assumes the value 1 at this point, while point 2 corresponds to a function assuming the value 0 at point 1. These functions are distinct. We take our set B to be the set of all functions on A with values 0 and 1.

Thus, the cardinality of set B is not less than the cardinality of set A. Let us now show that these cardinalities are not equal, i.e., no one-to-one correspondence can be found between the elements of sets A and B. Indeed, suppose such a correspondence existed.

Let us then designate the function corresponding to element a of A by $f_a(x)$. Remember that all the functions $f_a(x)$ assume only the two values 0 and 1.

Let us define a new function $\varphi(x)$ by means of the equation:

$$\varphi(x) = 1 - f_x(x) \tag{3.32}$$

Thus, in order to determine the value of the function $\varphi(x)$ at some point a of A we first must find the function $f_a(x)$ corresponding to this point and subtract its value at $x = a$ from 1. It is now clear that the function $\varphi(x)$ is defined on the set A and assumes only the values 0 and 1. Consequently, $\varphi(x)$ is an element of set B. But then by our assumption $\varphi(x)$ corresponds to some point b of A; this means that

$$\varphi(x) = f_b(x) \tag{3.33}$$

It follows from Eqs. (3.26) and (3.27) that for all x in A

$$1 - f_x(x) = f_b(x) \tag{3.34}$$

Let us set $x = b$ in this equation. Then we get

$$1 - f_b(b) = f_b(b) \tag{3.35}$$

so that

$$f_b(b) = \tfrac{1}{2} \tag{3.36}$$

But this contradicts the requirement that the values of the function $f_b(x)$ be 0 and 1. The contradiction we have obtained shows that there can be no one-to-one correspondence between sets A and B.

Thus, given any set A, we can construct a set B of larger cardinality. Therefore, no set of largest cardinality can exist.

Let us note that the set B can be constructed in other ways. For instance, B can be taken to be the set of all subsets of set A. Indeed, let C be some subset of A. We choose a function $f(x)$ on A which assumes the value 1, if $x \in C$, and the value 0, if $x \notin C$. Clearly, distinct subsets give rise to distinct functions. On the other hand, each function $f(x)$ which assumes the values 0 and 1 corresponds to the subset of A composed of those elements x for which the function is 1. We have thus set up a one-to-one correspondence between the set of functions defined on set A and assuming the values 0 and 1 and the set of all subsets of A.

The Arithmetic of the Infinite

We have now learned something about the cardinalities of various sets. The concept of cardinality, as we mentioned earlier, is a generalization of the concept of number of elements in a finite set. Now, we can carry out certain arithmetic operations on the natural numbers—we can add, subtract and multiply them. These operations may be regarded as parallels of certain operations on sets. For example, the addition of natural numbers corresponds to the addition of two nonintersecting finite sets. If there are m elements in one set and n elements in the other, then there will be $m + n$ elements in their sum.

Operations on cardinalities are defined analogously. Here we shall employ special symbols to denote the cardinalities. For example, we denote the cardinality of a countable set by $\aleph_0$ ($\aleph$ is the first letter of the Hebrew alphabet and is called *aleph*). We denote the cardinality of the continuum by $\mathfrak{c}$ (Gothic $\mathfrak{c}$), the cardinality of the set of all functions defined on the real axis by $\mathfrak{f}$, etc.

We can add cardinalities just as we add natural numbers. Namely, if the cardinality of set A is $\mathfrak{m}$ and the cardinality of set B is $\mathfrak{n}$, where A and B do not intersect, then $\mathfrak{m} + \mathfrak{n}$ denotes the cardinality of the set $A + B$. It follows from the properties of the addition of sets that

$$\mathfrak{m} + \mathfrak{n} = \mathfrak{n} + \mathfrak{m} \tag{3.37a}$$

$$\mathfrak{m} + (\mathfrak{n} + \mathfrak{p}) = (\mathfrak{m} + \mathfrak{n}) + \mathfrak{p} \tag{3.37b}$$

However, many of the rules of addition for infinite cardinalities are quite unlike the ordinary rules of arithmetic. But this is scarcely surprising, for we already know that the properties of infinite sets are quite different from those of finite sets. For example, in the arithmetic of the infinite we have the identities:

$$n + \aleph_0 = \aleph_0 \tag{3.38}$$

$$\aleph_0 + \aleph_0 = \aleph_0 \tag{3.39}$$

$$\aleph_0 + \mathfrak{c} = \mathfrak{c} \tag{3.40}$$

$$\mathfrak{c} + \mathfrak{c} = \mathfrak{c} \tag{3.41}$$

$$\mathfrak{c} + \mathfrak{f} = \mathfrak{f} \tag{3.42}$$

The first rule tells us that the sum of a finite and a countable set is a countable set; the second tells us that the sum of two countable sets is a countable set; the third tells us that when we supplement a set of cardinality that of the continuum by a countable set, we get a set with the cardinality of the continuum. The reader can now easily interpret the remaining identities.

Next let us see how infinite cardinalities multiply. We must first decide what set operation is related to multiplication of the natural numbers. Let A be a finite set composed of m elements and let B be a finite set containing n elements.

We form a new set $A + B$, whose elements are all possible pairs (a, b) with $a \in A$ and $b \in B$. If we let $a_1, \ldots, a_m$ denote the elements of the first set and $b_1, \ldots, b_n$ denote the elements of the second set, then these pairs can be arranged in the form of a tabulation:

$$
\begin{array}{ccc}
(a_1, b_1) & \ldots & (a_1, b_n) \\
& \vdots & \\
(a_m, b_1) & \ldots & (a_m, b_n)
\end{array}
\qquad (3.43)
$$

It is clear from the tabulation that there are mn such pairs, i.e., they are equal in number to the product of the numbers m and n.

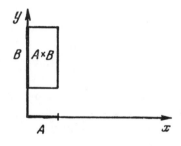

Let us carry this operation over to infinite sets. Let A and B be infinite sets. The set whose elements are all possiple pairs (a, b), $a \in A$, $b \in B$, is called their direct product and denoted by $A \times B$. For example, if A is the set of points of segment $[0, 1]$ and B is the set of points of segment $[1, 3]$, then we can represent $A \times B$ by the set of points of the rectangle sketched in Fig. 15. Indeed, each point of the rectangle corresponds to its two projections on the axes.

If set A has cardinality $\mathfrak{m}$ and set B has cardinality $\mathfrak{n}$, then $\mathfrak{mn}$ denotes the cardinality of the set $A \times B$. We have the following rules for the multiplication of cardinalities:

$$\mathfrak{mn} = \mathfrak{nm} \tag{3.44}$$

$$(\mathfrak{mn})\mathfrak{p} = \mathfrak{m}(\mathfrak{np}) \tag{3.45}$$

$$\mathfrak{m}(\mathfrak{n} + \mathfrak{p}) = \mathfrak{mn} + \mathfrak{mp} \tag{3.46}$$

Furthermore, we have the identities

$$\aleph_0\aleph_0 = \aleph_0 \tag{3.47}$$

$$\aleph_0\mathfrak{c} = \mathfrak{c} \tag{3.48}$$

$$\mathfrak{cc} = \mathfrak{c} \tag{3.49}$$

The first identity means that if A and B are countable sets, then the set of all pairs (a, b), $a \in A$, $b \in B$, is also countable. This is another formulation of the statement that the sum of a countable set of countable sets is itself a countable set. And the identity $\mathfrak{cc} = \mathfrak{c}$ means that the numbers of points in the interval and in the square are one and the same. For $\mathfrak{c}$ is the number of points in the interval, while $\mathfrak{cc}$ is the number of points in the square.

Infinite Exponents

Since we already know how to multiply cardinalities together, we can raise a cardinality to any power given by a natural number. But now we are going to explain how to take powers of cardinalities when the exponent is infinite, that is we are going to explain what the symbol $\mathfrak{n}^{\mathfrak{m}}$ means. To do this we must again go back to finite sets and describe a set with n^m elements.

This can be done as follows: Let set A contain m elements and let set B contain n elements. B^A is to denote the set of all possible functions defined on the set A with values in the set B. In other words, each element of the set B^A gives us a rule for assigning an element $b = f(a)$ from B to each element a of A. Suppose, for example, that the set A consists of the three numbers 1, 2, 3 and set B consists of two elements: the dot and the dash. Then the elements of set B^A consist of "functions" like $f(1) = \cdot$, $f(2) = \cdot$, $f(3) = -$, or $f(1) = -$, $f(2) = \cdot$, $f(3) = \cdot$. These "functions" can be written simply as sequences of dots and dashes, each sequence having three symbols. It is easy to see that there are 8 such sequences, i.e., 2^3. Namely, we have the sequences:

$$\cdots \quad \cdot\cdot- \quad \cdot-\cdot \quad \cdot-- \tag{3.50}$$
$$-\cdot\cdot \quad -\cdot- \quad --\cdot \quad ---$$

We found $8 = 2^3$ sequences. This is no accident. If the set A consists of m elements and the set B consists of n elements, then B^A contains n^m elements. We propose that the reader prove this for himself.

Now we are in a position to explain what we mean by the symbol n^m, where m and n are infinite cardinalities. Namely, we take a set A of cardinality m and a set B of cardinality n; we let B^A denote the set of all "functions" defined on A with values in B. n^m is the cardinality of this set.

We showed earlier that for any set A the cardinality of the set of functions defined on A with values 0 and 1 is greater than the cardinality of set A. This means that for any cardinality we have the inequality

$$2^m > m \tag{3.51}$$

Let us note in addition that

$$c = 2^{\aleph_0} \tag{3.52}$$

Indeed, we saw before that the set of all infinite telegrams had the cardinality of the continuum. But any infinite telegram is nothing more than a function defined on the set of natural numbers, which assumes only two values: dot and dash. Thus, the set of all infinite telegrams has cardinality $2^{\aleph_0}$. This proves equality (3.52).

On the Ordering of Numbers

The cardinalities of sets (or, as they are also called, *cardinal numbers*) do only half the work of the natural numbers. After all, the natural numbers can be applied to answer not only the question "how many?", but also to answer the question "in which place does it come?" In other words, we speak not only of "two," "five," "twenty," but also of "second," "fifth," "twentieth." But the cardinality tells us nothing about the order of the elements. And even though the set of natural numbers has as many elements as the set of integers, they are ordered in quite different ways. The set of natural numbers has a first element, while the set of integers has no first element.

The cardinal numbers therefore yield insufficient knowledge for the study of the order of arrangement of the elements in a set; we need new concepts for this purpose. We first introduce the concept of *ordered set*. We say that a set A is ordered, if for every pair of its elements a relation of inequality has been defined which possesses the following properties:

(1)   if $a < b$, then $a \neq b$;
(2)   if $a < b$ and $b < c$, then $a < c$.

It is easy to order the set of all real numbers, the set of all rational numbers, the set of all natural numbers, etc.

An ordering can also be introduced for the set of all complex numbers. Namely, we can say that $a + bi < c + di$, if either $a < c$, or $a = c$ and $b < d$. For example, $2 + 15i < 3 + 10i$, $2 + 4i < 2 + 5i$. The set of all polynomials can be ordered in an analogous fashion. Of course, different notions of ordering can be introduced into the same set.

For instance, consider the set of all the distinct words occurring in this book. This set might be ordered as follows: take the book and while reading it write down all the words appearing in it in the order in which you encounter them. In this case we can state the rule of ordering as follows: word A precedes word B, if word A is encountered earlier than word B when the book is read.

However, we can proceed in another way: agree that word A precedes word B; if word A precedes word B in the alphabetical ordering. Clearly, these form two distinct ways of ordering the same set.

We say that two ordered sets A and B have the same *order type*, if we can set up a one-to-one correspondence between them which preserves the order of the elements. In other words, if $a_1 \leftrightarrow b_1$ and $a_2 \leftrightarrow b_2$, then $a_1 < a_2$ implies that $b_1 < b_2$.

For example, any two segments of the real line have the same order type. The mapping shown in Fig. 11 preserves the order of the points. The mapping of the whole line onto the open interval (the segment with endpoints removed) shown in Fig. 12 also preserves order. But the segment and the real line have different order types. Although we can set up a one-to-one correspondence between them, this correspondence must disturb the ordering—after all, the segment has initial and final points, while the line has none.

Completely Ordered Sets

Even countable sets can be ordered in the most varied ways. Indeed, the sets of natural numbers, integers and rational numbers are countable and these sets are all ordered differently. The set of natural numbers has a first element (the number 1), while neither the set of integers nor the set of rational numbers has a first element. On the other hand, in both the sets of natural numbers and integers we can point out pairs of elements between which no other element of the set occurs (for example, the numbers 5 and 6), while in the set of rational numbers we can always find infinitely many elements of the set between any two elements.

In order to learn something about these varied orderings G. Cantor singled out a special class of ordered sets, some of whose properties were quite similar to those of the natural numbers. If we choose a nonempty subset of the natural numbers, then we can always find a least element, or leftmost element, among its members. G. Cantor gave the name of well-ordered sets to sets possessing this property. In other words, an ordered set A is said to be *well-ordered*, if each of its nonempty subsets has a first element.

As we have already indicated, the simplest example of a well-ordered set is the set of natural numbers. We can represent it by means of the points $1, 2, 3, \ldots$ on the half line $(0, \infty)$. Now, the mapping of the line onto the open interval shown in Fig. 12 preserves the order of the points. It maps the half line $(0, \infty)$ into the interval $(0, 1)$. Thus, we can choose points in the interval $(0, 1)$ instead of the points $1, 2, 3 \ldots$. We get an infinite set of points $a_1, a_2, \ldots, a_n, \ldots$ converging on the point 1 (Fig. 16a).

Now consider the point 1. We cannot use ordinary numbers to number this point—we have used these up in numbering the points $a_1, \ldots, a_n, \ldots$. We therefore need a new number, not a natural number, to index this point.

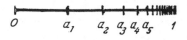

Fig. 16a.

Since the point 1 lies beyond all the points which we were able to index using the natural numbers, we call this new number "transfinite" (from the Latin meaning "beyond the finite"). The symbol ω has been adopted to denote the transfinite number immediately following the natural numbers $1, 2, 3, \ldots$. We therefore denote 1 by a_ω. The set A of all points $a_1, \ldots, a_n, \ldots, a_\omega$ is also a well ordered set. (Try to show this!)

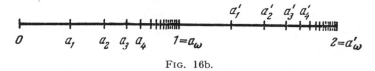

Fig. 16b.

We now shift all the points of set A one unit to the right. The point a_1 becomes point $a_1' = a_1 + 1$, point a_2 becomes point $a_2' = a_2 + 1$, etc. As a result we obtain a set B composed of the points $a_1', \ldots, a_n', \ldots, a_\omega'$. It is not difficult to show that the set $A + B$ is well ordered. Let us try to number its elements. We already know how to number the points of set A. Since point a_1' follows directly after point a_ω (Fig. 16b), it is natural to index it with the transfinite number $\omega + 1$, i.e., set $a_1' = a_{\omega+1}$. In the same way, it is natural to index the following point, i.e., a_2', with the transfinite number $\omega + 2$, etc. Now the point a_ω' comes after all the points $a_{\omega+1}, \ldots, a_{\omega+n}, \ldots$ so for it we use the transfinite number 2ω:

$$a_\omega{}' = a_{2\omega} \tag{3.53}$$

The reader has probably already guessed that we are now going to shift the points of set A two units to the right in order to get the new points which we will have to index with the transfinite numbers $2\omega + 1, \ldots, 2\omega + n, \ldots, 3\omega$. Continuing in this way, we find a well-ordered set composed of points indexed by transfinite numbers of the form $k\omega + n$, where k and n are natural numbers.

But this does not complete the construction of transfinite numbers. We have again obtained a set distributed over the half line $(0, \infty)$, and infinitely many points of our set are located on each segment $[n, m + 1]$. Let us now again map the half line $(0, \infty)$ on the interval $(0, 1)$. We get a set of points converging to the point 1. We again need a new transfinite number to index the point 1; this time it will be ω^2. We can now go on to construct the transfinite numbers $\omega^2 + 1, \ldots, \omega^3, \ldots, \omega^n, \ldots$ and even ω^ω. There is even a transfinite number:

But we are not going to dwell any longer on these questions.

The Enigmatic Axiom

We have already said that some sets can be ordered in different ways. But is it always possible to order a given set;

and if it is always possible, can the set always be made into a well-ordered set? Many mathematicians have worked on this problem—after all, it follows that if the answer is yes, any set can be indexed with the help of transfinite numbers.

An unexpectedly simple and short solution was published in 1904 by Zermelo—he was able to show that any set can be well ordered (G. Cantor had already conjectured this in 1883). However, Zermelo's proof did not satisfy all mathematicians. The problem was that the proof depended on one assumption which appeared to be far from obvious to both its author and others. This statement came to be called the *axiom of choice* or *Zermelo's axiom* and can be illustrated as follows:

Suppose that in front of you lay several piles of apples. It is obvious that you could select an apple from each pile and put them in a new pile. It would also seem to be true that the same could be done if there were infinitely many apples in each pile as well as infinitely many piles. This is what constitutes the axiom of choice:

If an infinite set of infinite sets is given, then it is possible to choose one element from each set without giving the rule of choice in advance.

Indeed, all the trouble arises from these last words—the axiom of choice leads to completely nonconstructive proofs: with it you can prove, for example, that every set can be well ordered, but it does not give any information about how to go about it.

Mathematicians employed the axiom of choice for many years, considering it to be completely obvious. But when they began to reflect on it more deeply, it came to appear more and more mysterious. Many of the theorems proved with the help of the axiom of choice completely contradict

our mathematical intuition.   This led the well-known
mathematician Bertrand Russell to speak of this axiom as
follows:

"At first it seems obvious, but the more you think about
it, the stranger the deductions from this axiom seem to
become; in the end you cease to understand what is meant
by it."

Nevertheless, the majority of mathematicians make use
of the axiom of choice in their studies without any qualms.

Two Apples from One

Let us talk about one of the most surprising consequences
of the axiom of choice.   Probably everyone has seen a clever
magician at work on the stage.   First he shows the spectators
an empty sack, then he drops a ball into the sack, only to
draw out ... two; dropping in the two balls, he pulls out
four; dropping in the four, he pulls out eight.   Of course,
everyone knows that it is no miracle, but is simply "sleight
of hand."   Such miracles can, however, happen in the theory
of sets.

We take an ordinary apple and divide it in any way into
four pieces.   It seems clear that if we take only two of the
pieces, it will not be possible to form an entire apple from
them (in the same way, if you have eaten half an orange, you
cannot form an entire orange from the remaining slices).

However, mathematicians can divide a sphere into four
equal parts in such a way that an entire sphere of the same
radius can be formed from two of the parts, without sup-
plementing them in any way, simply by translating them as
rigid bodies.   A second, identical sphere can be formed from
the other two parts.   Thus, we can obtain two distinct

spheres from the one. It is a pity that this problem is only capable of being solved in theory, otherwise we could make two apples from one, then four, then eight, etc. Of course, the problem cannot be solved in the real world—it would contradict the law of conservation of matter.

Fig. 17.

Such a division of the sphere into four parts is based on the axiom of choice.

At this time we shall not speak further of other, equally strange consequences of this axiom.

4

Remarkable Functions and Curves, or a Stroll through a Mathematical Art Museum

How the Notion of Function Developed

The majority of mathematical concepts underwent a long period of development. They first arose as generalizations of intuitive ideas derived from everyday experience. With gradual removal of special and accidental aspects, these intuitive ideas slowly crystallized into exact mathematical definitions. But it often happened that these definitions applied not only to those objects whose study led to their formulation, but also to other objects that had not been thought about earlier. The study of these new objects was begun and the process of abstraction was carried to ever higher levels; next came the extension of the original definitions on the basis provided by the studies. Ever broader meaning came to be attributed to mathematical concepts; they embraced wider and wider classes of objects, occurring in more varied fields of mathematics.

The concept of number, for example, underwent such a long period of development, starting in prehistoric times when people could only count "one, two, many," and, carrying on to our own time: natural numbers, fractions, negative numbers, complex numbers, quaternions, hypercomplex numbers,.... And it must be admitted that not every new generalization of this or that concept was enthusiastically received by all mathematicians. For example, for a long time not only the complex but even the negative numbers were not recognized as real by many mathematicians.

The notion of function also followed a tortuous path. The idea of the interdependence of two quantities apparently arose in classical Greek science. But here the quantities were only of a geometric nature. Even Newton, one of the founders of mathematical analysis, employed only geometric language in his discussion of interdependent quantities. Although the notion of function had actually been in use since the days of Fermat and Descartes, the term "function" itself only came into being in 1694, first appearing in the works of the German mathematician Leibniz. He and Newton share the credit for the foundations of the calculus. But Leibniz's notion of function was a very narrow one: he named the abscissa, ordinate, subtangent and subnormal, radius of curvature and other line segments related to a definite point on a curve, and said that a certain kind of dependence existed between any two of these. Thus, Leibniz too restricted function to the realm of geometry. It was only in 1718 that Leibniz's student J. Bernoulli gave a definition of function free of geometric language:

A function of a variable quantity is a magnitude formed in some manner from this variable quantity and constants.

The next step in the development of the concept of function is linked to the name of Leonhard Euler of the Petersburg Academy, a brilliant student of J. Bernoulli. He defined function thus in his "Differential Calculus":

Quantities dependent on others such that as the second change, so do the first, are said to be functions.

However, Euler and the other mathematicians of his time required that a function must be expressible by means of a formula. From the point of view of the mathematicians of the 18th century the expression:

$$y = \begin{cases} x, & \text{if} \quad x < 0 \\ x^2, & \text{if} \quad x > 0 \end{cases} \qquad (4.1)$$

defines not one, but two functions.

It soon became clear that the matter was significantly more complex. When he solved the problem of the vibrating string, D. Bernoulli obtained an answer in the form of what is called a *trigonometric series*. We shall not discuss these here, but only say that the shape of the string is given by a single formula (although one containing an infinite number of terms).

This same problem of the vibrating string was solved by the French mathematician d'Alembert. d'Alembert's solution had a form quite different from that of Bernoulli's, and, what is most important, could be given by different formulas for different values of the argument.

What looked to be an insoluble contradiction now loomed up before 18th century mathematics: two answers had been obtained for the same problem, one expressed by a single formula for all values of the argument and another by several formulas. D. Bernoulli's solution was questioned because of this: it was thought that he had not found all solutions to the problem, just the solutions expressible in a single formula. A bitter controversy arose in which all the prominent mathematicians of the 18th century, Euler, d'Alembert, and others, took part.

The controversy, in essence, was over the concept of function, the connection between the functional dependence and the possibility of expressing this dependence by means of a formula. A definitive solution to the question was obtained at the beginning of the 19th century, when the French mathematician J. Fourier showed that the sum of an infinite series of trigonometric functions can be expressed by different formulas over different intervals. He then gave a new definition of function, stressing that the main thing was the assignment of values for the function; whether this assignment was carried out by means of a single formula or not was unimportant.

Fourier's result was refined by the German mathematician Dirichlet, who showed that any given curve could be the graph of the sum of a trigonometric series. It was required only that the number of maxima and minima on the curve be finite and that the curve be finite and bounded in amplitude. Dirichlet also refined Fourier's definition of function and gave it the form in which it is employed today (quite similar definitions were given somewhat earlier than Dirichlet's by Lacroix, Lobachevsky, and other mathematicians). Dirichlet's definition reads:

A variable quantity y is said to be a function of a variable quantity x, if to each value of the quantity x there corresponds a uniquely determined value of the quantity y.

Later on the words "belonging to some set" were added to the words "each value of the quantity x" (after all, the function does not have to be defined for all values of x).

This definition was extremely general: not a word was said about the necessity of giving the function by means of a single formula holding over the whole domain of definition. Moreover, it need not even be given by any formula at all but could be defined in words. For example, Dirichlet himself studied the function:

$$f(x) = \begin{cases} 0, & \text{if } x \text{ is an irrational number} \\ 1, & \text{if } x \text{ is a rational number} \end{cases} \qquad (4.2)$$

This definition did not specify a function according to the viewpoint of 18th century mathematicians; for no formula was given which would allow one to compute the values of *Dirichlet's function*. Nevertheless, this definition completely determines the function. It is quite clear that, for example, $f(\tfrac{3}{4}) = 1$ while $f(\sqrt{2}) = 0$.

Dirichlet's definition, in essence, was definitive (with the indicated refinement) for numerical functions of a numerical argument. Further developments consisted in considering functions defined on arbitrary sets and assuming their values on arbitrary sets. Indeed, suppose we are given two sets A and B and suppose that an element b of B has been placed in correspondence with each element a of A. Then we say that a function has been defined on set A with values in set B. In this very general formulation, the notion of function merges with those of *correspondence*, mapping and transformation.

For example, from this point of view the area of a triangle is a function defined on the set of all triangles and assuming its values in the set of positive numbers. And the circle inscribed in a triangle is a function defined on the set of all triangles with values in the set of circles. But here we are not going to maintain such a general viewpoint; we shall restrict our interest to functions defined on sets of numbers and assuming numerical values.

The Genie Escapes from the Bottle

Dirichlet's definition allows functions to have very odd properties. Before, if one wanted to construct a function with some unusual property, one had to spend a long time combining different formulas, but now the job was much simpler. It was now possible to construct and study various functions without worrying about whether they could be expressed by formulas. And for the last half century functions have been constructed with properties completely at variance with those of the "well-behaved" functions. Truly, even Dirichlet himself did not believe that such "monsters" could exist.

Dirichlet's own function, of which we spoke earlier, was already unusual. After all, there are infinitely many rational and irrational numbers on even the smallest interval of the x axis. But Dirichlet's function is one for rational numbers and zero for irrational numbers. Thus, as we move along the x axis, the value of the function constantly jumps back and forth between 0 and 1. It is impossible to graph this function, since it is discontinuous at every point.

And even among the continuous functions are some with unexpected properties. For example, can a continuous function have infinitely many maxima and minima on a finite interval? This seems impossible at first glance. After all, the curve has to take up space in falling from a maximum to a minimum, then again rising to a maximum, etc. How can it do all this in a finite interval? Nevertheless, such odd functions do exist and it is quite simple to construct one.

We shall construct such a function on the segment [0, 1]. We first cut the segment in two and construct an equilateral triangle on the left half. Now we divide the right half into two equal parts and construct a second equilateral triangle on the segment $[\frac{1}{2}, \frac{3}{4}]$. We carry out the described operation infinitely many times. As a result we find a mountain range with infinitely many peaks gradually dropping down to the point 1 (Fig. 18). We take the curve obtained as the graph of the function $f(x)$. Thus, the function is defined at each point of the segment [0, 1] with the exception of the right endpoint 1. Here we put $f(1) = 0$.

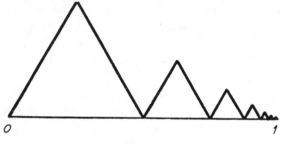

FIG. 18.

Since the height of the peaks approaches 0 as x approaches 1, we obtain a function continuous at all points of the segment [0, 1]. But the number of maxima and minima on this segment is infinite!

In order to construct such a strange function a mathematician of the 18th century would have to spend a lot of time trying out combinations of functions before he would conjecture that the function

$$f(x) = \begin{cases} x \cos \dfrac{\pi}{x}, & \text{if } \quad x \neq 0 \\[2mm] 0, & \text{if } \quad x = 0 \end{cases} \tag{4.3}$$

had infinitely many maxima and minima on the segment [0, 1] (Fig. 19).

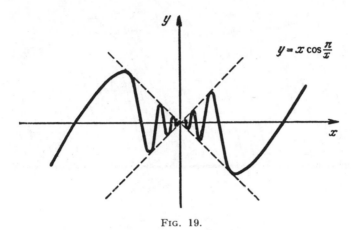

$$y = x \cos \frac{\pi}{x}$$

Fig. 19.

Fig. 19.

But functions with infinitely many maxima and minima were only the first of the unpleasant surprises in store for mathematicians. The genie had only begun to escape from the bottle.

Wet Points

The function we constructed in the preceding section had only one point near which there were infinitely many maxima and minima; this was the point 1. Now we shall construct another function with many more such points.

Imagine that rain is falling on the segment [0, 1] of the x axis. We go about providing shelter from the rain as follows. We divide the segment [0, 1] into three equal parts and erect a tent in the form of an equilateral triangle in the central part. It protects all the points of the central

part from the rain (except the endpoints, i.e., the points
⅓ and ⅔).

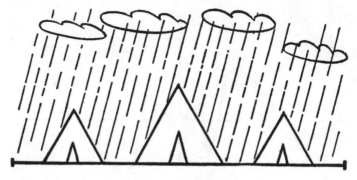

FIG. 20.   It is raining.

Now we divide each of the two pieces left over into three
parts and protect the central part with a tent of the same
form (but only half as wide).   We now have the curve
sketched in Fig. 21.   In the third step of this procedure we
erect four more tents, then eight more, etc.

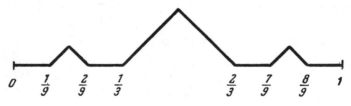

FIG. 21.

Now we come to the question of whether all the points of
the segment have been sheltered by the saw-toothed curve,
or whether there remain points wet by the rain? It is easy
to point out some of the "wet" points—these are the endpoints of the sheltered segments (i.e., such points as 1/3,

2/3, 1/9, 2/9, 7/9, 8/9, etc.). All these points were left unprotected when the corresponding tents were erected, and
they remain unprotected by the tents erected subsequently.
It is easy to see that there are infinitely many such endpoints,
but that they still form only a countable set.

But it turns out that there is an uncountable set of "wet"
points in addition to these. It is convenient to use the
ternary representation in order to describe them. As we
know, the ternary representation is formed in the same way
as the decimal representation, except that the numbers are
grouped in threes instead of tens. Thus, in the ternary
representation we only employ the three digits 0, 1, 2 for
writing numbers in place of the ten ordinarily used.

It is easy to learn how to change the representation of a
number whose ternary representation is

$$0.02020202\ldots$$

It is represented in the decimal system by the infinite
geometric progression:

$$\frac{2}{3^2} + \frac{2}{3^4} + \frac{2}{3^6} + \cdots \tag{4.4}$$

The sum of this progression is $\frac{1}{4}$. Thus,

$$\tfrac{1}{4} = 0.020202\ldots \tag{4.5}$$

Now we can say exactly which points remain wet after
all the protective tents have been set up. The first tent
shelters the points lying between $\frac{1}{3}$ and $\frac{2}{3}$. But these are
just the points whose ternary representations have the form

$$0.1\ldots \tag{4.6}$$

where the dots stand for any combination of digits 0, 1, 2
(in the same way that all the points whose decimal representa-

tions begin with the digit 1, i.e., have the form 0.1..., lie between the points 1/10 and 2/10).

Those points still wet after the first step are those whose ternary representations have the form

$$0.0\ldots \tag{4.7}$$

or the form

$$0.2\ldots \tag{4.8}$$

We can prove in the same way that after the two tents of the second step have been set up the points remaining wet are only those whose ternary representations begin with one of the following four combinations:

$$0.00\ldots$$
$$0.02\ldots$$
$$0.20\ldots \tag{4.9}$$
$$0.22\ldots$$

Thus, any point in whose ternary representation a one occurs will at some stage be protected from the rain. In the end only those points remain wet whose ternary representations can be written without using 1. For example, the points

$$\tfrac{1}{4} = 0.020202\ldots \tag{4.10}$$

and

$$\tfrac{3}{4} = 0.20202\ldots \tag{4.11}$$

remain wet.

But now it must be clear why the set of "wet" points has the cardinality of the continuum. After all, this set can be put into one-to-one correspondence with the set of infinite telegrams [see (3.20)]. We can do this by putting each point of the form

$$0.20220200\ldots \tag{4.12}$$

in correspondence with an infinite telegram by replacing 0 by the dot and 2 by the dash. Different numbers correspond to different telegrams when this procedure is followed. We already know that the set of infinite telegrams has the cardinality of the continuum; thus, the set of wet points will also have this cardinality.

The set of points we called wet was first constructed by Cantor, and is now called *Cantor's set*. It is clear from the construction of the tents that there are infinitely many maxima and minima of the saw-toothed curve near each point of Cantor's set.

The Devil's Staircase

There is still another interesting function related to Cantor's set. It is defined as follows. We first divide the segment [0, 1] into three equal parts and stipulate that our function equal $\frac{1}{2}$ at each point of the middle third. Then we divide the left and right thirds into three equal parts and stipulate that the function equal $1/4$ from $1/9$ to $2/9$, and equal $3/4$ from $7/9$ to $8/9$. We now have four segments on which the function is not yet defined:

$$\left[0, \frac{1}{9}\right] \qquad \left[\frac{2}{9}, \frac{1}{3}\right] \qquad \left[\frac{2}{3}, \frac{7}{9}\right] \qquad \left[\frac{8}{9}, 1\right] \tag{4.13}$$

We divide each of these into three equal parts and set the function equal to $1/8$, $3/8$, $5/8$, $7/8$, respectively, on the four middle pieces.

Continuing this process, we obtain a function which is defined on all the "dry" points, i.e., on all the points not belonging to Cantor's set. It is easy to define it on the points of this set too, and in such a way that it becomes continuous and nondecreasing on the segment [0, 1]. An approximation to the graph of the function obtained is shown in Fig. 22. It has the form of a staircase with an infinite number of steps (not all the steps are shown on the graph).

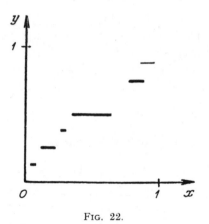

Fig. 22.

Of course, after learning about curves with infinitely many maxima and minima, we are not likely to be surprised at a staircase with an infinite number of steps. But here is something surprising. Let us compute the total length of our staircase. The first step has length 1/3, the next two have length 1/9 apiece, the next four have length 1/27 apiece, etc. Thus, the sum of the lengths of all the steps is expressed by the infinite geometric progression:

$$\frac{1}{3} + \frac{2}{9} + \frac{4}{27} + \cdots \qquad (4.14)$$

The sum of this progression is

$$\frac{\frac{1}{3}}{1 - \frac{2}{3}} = 1 \tag{4.15}$$

Hence, the total length of the staircase is 1. But the function does not increase at all along these steps; all its rising is concentrated at the points of Cantor's set. But very "few" points fall to the share of this set—even though its cardinality is that of the continuum, its length is zero! (The length of the segment [0, 1] is 1 and the total length of the steps is 1). Thus, our function manages somehow to rise from 0 to 1, even though it only increases on a set of zero length and never makes any jumps! Isn't this really surprising?

A Prickly Curve

For a period extending over many centuries mathematicians dealt only with curves at each point of which a tangent could be constructed. If there were exceptions these occurred at only a few points. The curve seemed to break

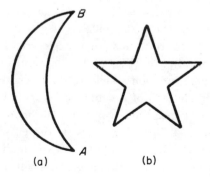

(a)   (b)

Fɪɢ. 23.

at these points, and they were therefore called *points of fracture*. The curve drawn in Fig. 23a has *two points of fracture*, while the curve drawn in Fig. 23b has ten *points of fracture*.

But the curve that we just now constructed already has infinitely many *points of fracture*: the curve in Fig. 19 has a countable set of such points, while the curve in Fig. 20 has a whole continuum of them. It breaks at each point of the Cantor set and, in addition, at the peaks of all the triangles. However, even the curve of Fig. 21 has breaks on a comparatively "small" set of points: its length is zero.

For a long time no mathematician believed that there could exist a continuous curve wholly composed of "saw-teeth," "breaks" and "prickles." Mathematicians were greatly amazed, therefore, when someone succeeded in constructing such a curve, and what is more, a function with a graph like a picket fence. The first to do this was the Czech mathematician Bolzano. But his work remained unpublished for a long time, and the first published example was that of the German mathematician K. Weierstrass. However, it is difficult for us to present Weierstrass' example, for it is based on the theory of trigonometric series.

We shall now discuss Bolzano's example, making a few slight changes. We first divide the segment $[0, 1]$ into four equal parts and construct an isosceles right triangle over the two central parts (Fig. 24a). The resulting curve is the graph of some function which we shall denote by $y = f_1(x)$. We next divide each of the four pieces again into four equal parts and correspondingly construct four more isosceles right triangles (Fig. 24b). This gives us the graph of a second function $y = f_2(x)$. If we add these two functions, the graph of the sum $y = f_1(x) + f_2(x)$ has the form sketched in Fig. 24c. It is clear that this curve already has more breaks and that these breaks are more densely distributed. In the next stage we again divide each piece into four parts, now constructing 16 isosceles right triangles and then adding the corresponding function $y = f_3(x)$ to the function $y = f_1(x) + f_2(x)$.

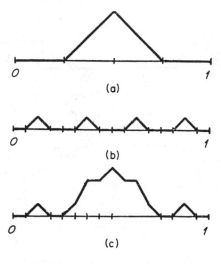

(a)

(b)

(c)

Fig. 24.

As we continue this process, we obtain a curve with a larger and larger number of breaks. In the limit we obtain a curve with a break at each point and possessing a tangent at no point.

A similar example of a curve possessing a tangent at no point was constructed by the Dutch mathematician Van der Waerden. He took an equilateral triangle, divided each of its sides into three equal parts and then constructed new equilateral triangles with peaks pointing out over the three central sections. This gave him a figure something like a sixpointed star (Fig. 25a). He then went on to divide each of the twelve sides of this star into three equal parts, again constructing equilateral triangles. This gave the even more prickly curve drawn in Fig. 25b. After infinitely many divisions and constructions of right triangles he obtained a curve at each point of which there was a break or a prickle.

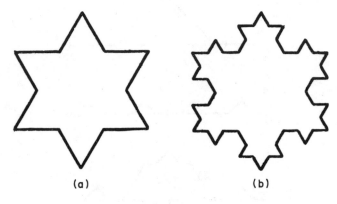

(a)   (b)

Fig. 25.

Mathematicians constructed many continuous functions whose graphs possess a tangent at no point and began to study their properties. These properties have no similarity to those of the "well-behaved" smooth functions with which they had dealt up to that time. It is no wonder, then, that mathematicians trained in the classical tradition regarded these new functions with astonishment. Going even beyond this, the prominent exponent of classical analysis Charles Hermite wrote as follows to his friend, the Dutch mathematician Stieltjes:

"I turn away in horror from this regrettable plague of continuous functions that do not have a derivative at even one point" (i.e., as we have named them, everywhere prickly curves).

The famous French mathematician H. Poincaré wrote:

"In the old days there was some practical purpose behind the search for new functions. Now functions are invented

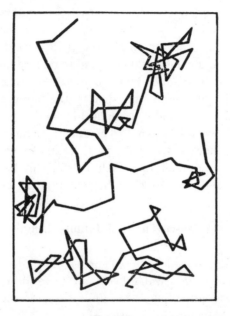

Fig. 26.

specifically for pointing up gaps in the reasoning of our predecessors; no other conclusion can be drawn from them except this."

But the later development of the science showed Poincaré to be wrong. In physics we encounter curves highly reminiscent of the everywhere prickly curves of Van der Waerden and others.   These curves are the trajectories of particles undergoing Brownian motion caused by collisions with molecules.   The French scientist Fr. Peppin made a sketch of the motion of these particles.   He observed their positions every 30 seconds and connected the points thus obtained with straight line segments.   His result was a tangle of broken lines something like that sketched in Fig. 26.   But it should not be thought that the particles observed actually moved in straight lines between the separate observations. If Peppin had observed them every half second instead of every half minute, he would have had to replace each straight line segment by a much more complicated broken line like that in Fig. 26.   And the shorter the interval between observations, the more complicated and "prickly" the broken line would become.   The American mathematician N. Wiener showed that if the particles in Brownian motion are sufficiently small that their inertia can be neglected, they move along curves which have no tangent at any point.

A Closed Curve of Infinite Length

We have often encountered curves of infinite length: the straight line, the parabola, etc all have infinite length. But all these curves go off to infinity, so it is not surprising that they have infinite length.   However, it is not difficult to construct a curve entirely contained in a finite region of the plane and still having infinite length.   For this we can take a circle and wind a spiral with infinitely many turns around it (Fig. 27).   Since the number of turns is infinite and the length of each turn is greater than that of the circumference of the circle, the length of the spiral must be infinite.

But can we construct a closed curve of infinite length?
The ordinary closed curves: the circle, the ellipse, the

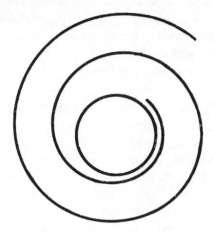

Fig. 27.

cardioid (Fig. 28) all have finite length. However, the length
of Van der Waerden's prickly curve is infinite.

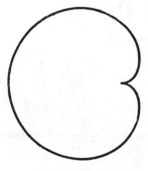

Fig. 28.

Indeed, the perimeter of the original triangle is **3**. As
is easily computed, the star obtained in the first stage has

length 4. And in the following stage we obtain a curve composed of 48 segments each of length 1/9. Thus its perimeter is 48/9. Next we obtain a curve of length 192/27, etc. In general, at nth stage we obtain a curve with perimeter $3 \cdot (\frac{4}{3})^n$. But this expression approaches infinity as n increases, so that the length of Van der Waerden's curve is infinite.

There are still other curves of infinite length. We construct the following curve as an example. We divide the segment [0, 1] in half and construct an isosceles triangle of altitude 1 on the left half. Next we divide the half [$\frac{1}{2}$, 1] into two equal parts and construct an isosceles triangle of altitude $\frac{1}{2}$ on the leftmost piece [$\frac{1}{2}$, $\frac{3}{4}$]. We construct the next isosceles triangle, again with altitude $\frac{1}{2}$, on the segment [3/4, 7/8]; the next four triangles are constructed with altitude $\frac{1}{4}$, etc (Fig. 29).

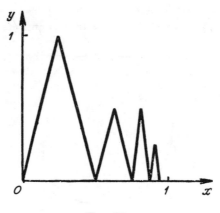

FIG. 29.

We again get a descending chain of mountains as in Fig. 18. But here the chain descends very slowly. It is clear that the length of each lateral side of the first triangle is greater than 1, of those of the second and third are greater than $\frac{1}{2}$, of those of the fourth, fifth, sixth, and seventh are greater than $\frac{1}{4}$, etc (the length of the lateral side is always greater than the altitude). Thus the length of the broken line is not less than the sum of the infinite series:

$$2 + \left(\frac{2}{2} + \frac{2}{2}\right) + \left(\frac{2}{4} + \frac{2}{4} + \frac{2}{4} + \frac{2}{4}\right) + \ldots \qquad (4.16)$$

But the sum of the numbers within each parenthetical expression is 2, and the number of parentheses is infinite; hence the sum of the series and the length of our curve are infinite.

A Mathematical Carpet

They tell how once Catherine the Second asked one of her generals what was the difference between a mortar and a howitzer. The embarassed general replied: "You see, Queenmother, a mortar is one thing and a howitzer is something else." We would probably receive an informative answer like this one if we were to ask a person knowing little about mathematics what is the difference between a curve, a surface, and a solid. Moreover, he would be surprised that we asked about such obvious things. After all, it is quite clear that a curve, a surface, and a solid are quite different things, and no one would call a circle a surface or a sphere a curve.

But a witty chess master once said that the difference between a master and a beginning chess player is that the beginner has everything clearly fixed in mind, while to the master everything is a mystery. That is also how matters stand with our question. Of course, when we are speaking of such geometric figures as a square or a circle, no one has any doubts about which is a curve and which is a surface. But in the course of mathematical development, since Cantor's discoveries, there have appeared many queer geometric figures, and even an experienced, knowledgeable professor, not to speak of a student, will not be able to decide right away whether they are curves, surfaces, or solids.

We shall present some of these figures. We take the segment [0, 1], divide it into 2 and erect a perpendicular of length $\frac{1}{2}$ at the center of the segment. Next we again divide each of the halves into 2 and construct a perpendicular, this time of length $\frac{1}{4}$, at each of the new points of division. Then we again divide the sections obtained into 2 parts and erect perpendiculars of length $\frac{1}{8}$ at the points of division.

Fig. 30.

After five such steps we obtain the figure drawn in Fig. 30. But we will not stop after five steps, but will continue our operation infinitely many times. The result is some geometric figure. Well, then, what is it, a curve or a surface? After all, we erected an infinite number of perpendiculars. Don't they solidify and fill up a small bit of surface near the segment [0, 1]? It is not too easy to answer this question.

And here is another example. We take a square of side 1 and divide it into 9 equal parts; then we discard the central part (leaving the sides of the square discarded). After this we divide each of the remaining squares into 9 equal squares, and again discard the central squares. After one more such operation we arrive at the figure drawn in Fig. 31 (the squares

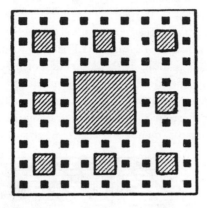

Fig. 31.

to be discarded are cross-hatched). It is clear that the figure in Fig. 31 is still a surface. But we will not stop at the third step; the squares will be divided into nine equal parts infinitely many times, and each time the central part will be discarded. In the end we obtain a geometric figure called *Sierpinski's carpet* after the Polish mathematician who devised it.

The figure looks like cloth woven by some mad weaver. The thread, frame and woof come from far and wide to be woven into a very symmetric and beautiful design. But the resulting carpet is full of holes—there is not an uncut piece in it; even the smallest square had to have its center cut out.

And it is not at all clear whether this carpet is a curve or a surface. After all, on the one hand, it does not contain a single solid piece, and so can hardly be called a surface; but, on the other hand, the threads forming it were woven into such a complex pattern that probably no one would unhesitatingly call Sierpinski's carpet a curve. In any case, it would be very hard to draw this "curve."

But Sierpinski's carpet is not the most complicated geometric figure. Instead of a square we could have taken a cube, divided it into 27 equal small cubes and discarded the central small cube along with its 6 neighboring cubes. Then we would have divided each small remaining cube into 27 equal parts and again would have carried out the operation of discarding certain parts (the solid remaining after two such operations is shown in Fig. 32). Suppose that the opera-

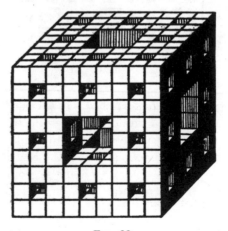

Fig. 32.

tion had been carried out infinitely many times. What kind of a figure would we get after all the pieces had been discarded—a curve, a surface or a solid?

Euclid Does Not Rely on Euclid

When a complicated geometric problem was placed before mathematicians of an earlier time, they first proceeded to examine what Euclid had written about it. After all, for almost two thousand years Euclid was the standard of mathematical rigor and an encyclopedia of geometric knowledge. It is significant that even philosophers striving to secure themselves from reproach regarding the rigor of their arguments, had recourse to Euclid's language and formulated their statements as axioms, lemmas, and theorems.

But as far as our question is concerned, everything Euclid wrote was entirely too vague. The first lines of Euclid's book "Elements" read as follows:

1. A point is that which has no parts.
2. A curve is length without width.
3. The extremity of a curve is a point.
4. A surface is that which has only length and width.
5. The extremity of a surface is a curve.
6. A boundary is that which is the extremity of something.
7. A figure is that which is contained within something or within some boundaries.

Now, like these or not, they are not rigorous mathematical definitions. A person not knowing what points, curves, or lines are will hardly get much useful information from these "definitions," so reminiscent of the answer of the confused general ("a curve is one thing, and a surface is something else"). And, in any case, we shall not succeed in finding out from these definitions whether Sierpinski's carpet is a curve or a surface, whether it has just length without width or both length and width.

However, such complicated figures as Sierpinski's carpet were unknown in Euclid's time, and definitions were not really necessary for simple figures—everyone could pick out which were the curves and which were the surfaces in a figure. It seems, though, that Euclid himself felt that all was not right with his definitions of the fundamental concepts. In any case, having presented these definitions in the beginning of the book, he went on to completely forget about them and did not employ them even once in the remainder of his work.

Are Rigorous Definitions Needed?

Euclid's authority stood unquestioned during the course of two thousand years. To doubt his statements in any way was to decisively and irrevocably undermine your own mathematical reputation. One of the greatest mathematicians of the 19th century, Karl Friedrich Gauss, arrived at the idea of a non-Euclidean geometry even before Lobachevsky, but did not publish his investigations, fearing, as he wrote one friend, the screams of the Boetians.* It was finally the mathematical exploit of the great Russian geometer Nikolai Ivanovich Lobachevsky, who did publish his discoveries in spite of the derision of the uncomprehending savants, that gave the world non-Euclidean geometry.

It became clear after the appearance of N. I. Lobachevsky's work that there existed two geometries, both irreproachable logically, but arriving at entirely different theorems. But if this is so, then every appeal to "geometric obviousness" completely lost its value. Each geometric assertion now had to be based on rigorous definitions and irreproachable

---

* A proverbially dull Greek tribe.

logical arguments. And now it was especially important that the fundamental geometric concepts of curve, figure, and solid be given exact definitions, in no way like those of the type "this is one thing, and that is something else."

This attempt at rigorous definition characterized not only the geometry, but also the analysis of the 19th century.

Science had succeeded in solving the most varied problems, from calculating the trajectory of an artillery shell to predicting the motions of planets and comets, with the aid of the differential and integral calculus based on the work of Newton, Leibniz, Euler, Lagrange, and other great mathematicians of the 17th and 18th centuries. But the fundamental concepts with whose aid these remarkable results were achieved were defined in a highly unrigorous manner. The mathematical analysis of that time was based on the concept of infinitesimal quantity, something balancing on the border of existence and nonexistence; something like zero, but not really zero. And mathematicians of the 18th century were forced to encourage their dubious students with the words: "Work, and belief will come to you."

But, really, mathematics is not religion; it cannot be founded on faith. And what was most important, the methods yielding such remarkable results in the hands of the great masters began to lead to errors and paradoxes when employed by their less talented students. The masters were kept from error by their perfect mathematical intuition, that subconscious feeling that often leads to the right answer more quickly than lengthy logical reasoning. But the students did not possess this intuition, and the end of the 18th century was marked by an unprecedented scandal in mathematics—an influx of formulas worth less than the paper they were printed on and questionable theorems whose domain of applicability was entirely unclear.

So, like children who break a beautiful toy in order to see what makes it work, the mathematicians of the 19th century subjected to a severe critique all the concepts employed up to that time and then began to rebuild mathematics on a foundation of rigorous definitions. Appeals to intuition were rejected; in place of this they demanded the most rigorous logic.* Found wanting in logic were the simple statements met with in a course in analysis, such as:
"Consider the domain G bounded by the closed curve Γ."

What is a closed curve? Why is it the boundary of a domain? Into how many parts does a closed curve divide the plane, and which of these parts is being studied?

The mathematicians of the 18th century did not reply to these questions. They just drew an oval and thought that this was all that needed to be said. But no one believed in pictures in the 19th century. The question "what is a curve?" was only one of the vital questions facing analysts.

However, a long time went by before they succeeded in giving a comprehensive answer to this question.

A Curve Is the Path of a Moving Point

In order to arrive at a rigorous definition of curve it was necessary to move away from the concrete objects on which the formation of the mathematical concept was based: long, thin threads; light rays; long, narrow roads, etc. In all these cases the length is so much greater than the width that the latter can be neglected. After mathematical idealization we arrive at the notion of length without width.

---

* True, they frequently tended to throw out the baby with the bath; in the 20th century much of what was thrown out became once more part of science.

The first to try to give a rigorous definition of curve was the French mathematician Camille Jordan. He proceeded from the fact that the trajectory of the motion of a very small body may be represented by a long, narrow tube. As we diminish the size of the body, the tube becomes more and more narrow and in the limit becomes the trajectory of a moving point—a curve possessing no width. Jordan applied this image in his definition of curve. Namely, he called the trajectory of a moving point a curve. Here the point is to move in a continuous manner, not making any jumps.

Jordan's definition can be more exactly stated as follows: In order to determine the position of a moving point its coordinates must be given for each moment during the motion. Since the motion takes place over a finite time interval, we can assume without loss of generality that this interval is [0, 1]. In other words, the point begins to move at some moment of time taken as the origin of the observation and completes its motion after a certain unit of time has elapsed (a second, a minute, a year, etc). The coordinates of the moving point are given for each moment of time t during the passing of this interval. Thus, the coordinates of the point depend on the moment of time t, and so are functions of t. We shall denote these functions by $f(t)$ and $g(t)$:

$$x = f(t) \qquad y = g(t) \qquad (4.17)$$

The requirement that the point move continuously amounts to the requirement that the functions $f(t)$ and $g(t)$ be continuous at each point of the segment [0, 1]. Roughly speaking, a small change in t should produce only a small change in the functions $f(t)$ and $g(t)$. More precisely, if $t_1, \ldots, t_n, \ldots$ approaches a value t, $\lim_{n \to \infty} t_n = t$, then we have the equalities

$$\lim_{n \to \infty} f(t_n) = f(t) \qquad (4.18)$$

and

$$\lim_{n \to \infty} g(t_n) = g(t) \qquad (4.19)$$

Jordan's definition turned out to be rather a successful one. All the curves with which mathematicians had dealt up to this time turned out to be curves in Jordan's sense, or, as is said, *Jordan curves*. Take, for example, a circle of radius 1. The length of this circle is 2π. So the point must move with speed 2π in order to complete the circle in unit time. Thus, in time t it will move through the arc $2\pi t$.

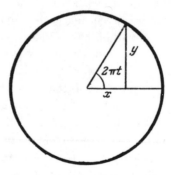

Fig. 33.

It is clear from Fig. 33 that its coordinates at time t must be given by the formulas

$$x = \cos 2\pi t$$
$$\qquad (4.20)$$
$$y = \sin 2\pi t$$

These equations are called the parametric equations of the circle. And for the curve sketched in Fig. 34 (it is called the *astroid*) the parametric equations have the form:

$$x = \cos^3 2\pi t$$
$$y = \sin^3 2\pi t \tag{4.21}$$

Jordan curves may be made up of several different curves. Let us take as an example the contour of a semidisc,

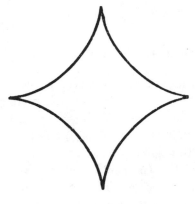

FIG. 34.

consisting of a semicircle of radius 1 and a diameter (Fig. 35). We let the moving point cover the semicircle in half the time and the diameter in the remaining half. We already know the expressions for the coordinates for motion along the circle. Under motion along the diameter, y remains

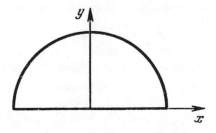

FIG. 35.

zero while x changes from -1 to 1. As a result we obtain the following parametric equations for the contour:

$$x = \begin{cases} \cos 2\pi t & \text{if} \quad 0 \leqslant t \leqslant \tfrac{1}{2} \\ 4t - 3 & \text{if} \quad \tfrac{1}{2} \leqslant t \leqslant 1 \end{cases} \tag{4.22}$$

$$y = \begin{cases} \sin 2\pi t & \text{if} \quad 0 \leqslant t \leqslant \tfrac{1}{2} \\ 0 & \text{if} \quad \tfrac{1}{2} \leqslant t \leqslant 1 \end{cases} \tag{4.23}$$

The Theorem Is Obvious, but the Proof Is Not

Employing his concept of curve, Jordan was successful in giving a precise meaning to the sentence from the analysis textbook that we spoke of earlier: "Let the closed curve Γ bound the domain G." A closed Jordan curve is a curve which passes through the point at $t = 1$ that was passed through at $t = 0$. The curve does not intersect itself as long as no two values of time t_1 and t_2 between 0 and 1 correspond to the same point on the curve.

Jordan proved the following theorem.

Theorem. *A closed Jordan curve Γ which does not intersect itself divides the plane into two parts. Two points contained in the same part can be connected by a broken line that does not intersect the curve Γ, but two points contained in different parts cannot be connected by such a broken line; any broken line connecting them must intersect the curve Γ* (Fig. 36).

This theorem seems completely obvious. Its proof, however, required very subtle arguments. Even when the curve Γ is the boundary of a polygon, the proof remains quite complicated. See if you can quickly decide whether or not the points A and B in Fig. 37 can be joined by a broken line which does not intersect the contour Γ.

The two parts into which a closed Jordan curve divides the plane are called the exterior and interior domains bounded by

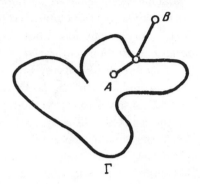

FIG. 36.

this curve. The concept of a domain bounded by a closed curve thus acquired an exact meaning.

FIG. 37.

A Curve Passing through All the Points of a Square

It appeared at first when Jordan gave his definition of curve that the goal had been achieved; a rigorous definition of the concept of curve was now available that did not depend on intuition. But it was quickly found out that this was not the case—Jordan's definition embraced not only what mathematicians usually called curves, but also geometric figures that no one would call curves. Mathematicians could somehow reconcile themselves to everywhere prickly curves, but no one had the heart to call a square a curve. But it did turn out that the square, the triangle, and the circle (not the perimeter of the figure, but in each case the figure itself with all its interior points) were curves in Jordan's sense. This was proved by the Italian mathematician Peano.

We already mentioned that Cantor set up a one-to-one correspondence between the points of the segment and those of the square, i.e., he showed that there are just as many points on the segment as are in the square. But his correspondence was not continuous. As the point moved along the segment, the corresponding point on the square did not crawl around like a beetle, but jumped around like a flea. Indeed, let us take the points

$$0.50000000\ldots\ 0.499999990000000\ldots \qquad (4.24)$$

on the segment. These points are quite close together. But the corresponding points on the square are far apart. For the point corresponding to the first of these is $(0.50000\ldots,$ $0.0000\ldots)$ situated on the bottom of the square, while the point corresponding to the second is $(0.4999000\ldots,$ $0.9999000\ldots)$ situated at the very top of the square. And if we increase the number of nines in the second point, thus bringing it closer to the first, the corresponding points on the square do not begin to approach one another.

Thus, Cantor's mapping of the segment onto the square, although one-to-one, was not continuous, and so did not give rise to a Jordan curve. Peano succeeded in setting up another mapping of the set of points of the segment onto the set of points of the square which sent neighboring points on the segment into neighboring points on the square. In other words, Peano was able to construct a curve (in Jordan's sense) which passed through all the points of the square!

Of course, we cannot draw Peano's curve, that is, unless we imitate an abstract painter and draw a black square. But, after all, the square is uniform, so we will not be able to see where the curve begins, where it ends and how it moves about the square. Therefore, we shall follow the example of the physicist Peppin, rather than that of the abstract painter, and sketch the position of the moving point using line segments. The shorter the intervals of time taken between separate "observations," the more accurately will the broken line thus obtained represent Peano's curve.

We shall first observe the position of the moving point every $\frac{1}{4}$ second. In other words, we observe its position at the beginning of the motion, at $\frac{1}{4}$ second after the beginning of the motion, at $\frac{1}{2}$ second after the beginning of the motion, at $\frac{3}{4}$ second and at the end of the motion. This gives us 5 points. Connecting them, we obtain the line ABCDE drawn in Fig. 38a.

Naturally, this line does not pass through all points of the curve. Now we reduce the interval of time between individual observations and observe the position of the point every 1/16 second. Now the curve twists more, the number of breaks increases and it takes the form sketched in Fig. 38b. If we observe the position of the moving point still more often, we obtain the curve sketched in Fig. 38c. We see that the curve fills the square more and more densely, that it approaches more and more closely to each of its points. In the limit, in which we would be constantly observing the moving point, we would obtain a curve passing through all points of the square without exception.

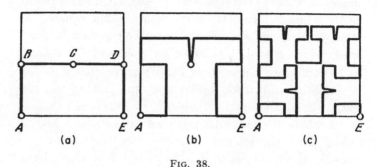

Fig. 38.

It should be noted that, while Peano has an advantage over Cantor in that his curve is continuous, he falls short in another respect. His curve no longer gave rise to a one-to-one mapping of the segment onto the line; it passed through some points of the square several times. It was later proved that it is impossible to obtain a correspondence that is both one-to-one and continuous: there does not exist a Jordan curve passing through all the points of the square exactly once!

Everything Had Come Unstrung

It is difficult to put into words the effect that Peano's result had on the mathematical world. It seemed that everything was in ruins, that all the basic mathematical concepts had lost their meaning; the difference between curve and surface, between surface and solid was no longer clear (the result showing the impossibility of a one-to-one continuous correspondence between the segment and the square was still unknown). The well-known French mathematician Henri Poincaré bitterly exclaimed:

"How was it possible that intuition could so deceive us?"

It soon became clear that Jordan's definition had its faults. On the one hand it was too broad: Peano's curve fits this definition; but on the other hand it was too narrow: not all the figures that we intuitively want to call curves satisfied this definition. For example, the curve sketched in Fig. 27, p. 105 (the circle with the spiral wrapped around it), is not a Jordan curve. And still other, more deeply hidden, failings were detected in Jordan's definition — after all, this definition did not just deal with the curve, but also dealt with the rate at which the point generating the curve moved. For example, imagine a runner who does the first half of the circle in $\frac{1}{4}$ minute, but then gets tired and takes $\frac{3}{4}$ minute to run the second half. Clearly, the parametric equations we get in this case are entirely different from (4.20) and (4.21).

And, after all, the point can traverse the circle in uncountably many ways, now speeding up, now slowing down. We thus obtain many different parametric equations for the same circle. It is very hard to guess that the equations

$$x = \frac{1 - t^2}{1 + t^2}$$

(4.25)

$$y = \frac{2t}{1 + t^2}$$

describe the same circle as the equations

$$x = \cos 2\pi t$$
$$y = \sin 2\pi t \tag{4.26}$$

And it would be quite easy to be confused by more complicated curves. Take, for instance, the two-leafed rose. We can traverse this curve as in Fig. 39a or as in Fig. 39b. From Jordan's point of view we would get two entirely different curves; but, after all, how we traverse the curve does not matter—the curve remains the same.

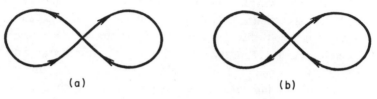

(a)   (b)

Fig. 39.

So the question was again raised: what is a curve and how does it differ from a surface? The answer was related to Cantor's general studies on geometric figures.

How to Make a Statue

Having founded the theory of sets, Cantor now turned his attention to the question: *what is a geometric figure*? The most general answer to this question would read: a geometric figure is any set of points in a space. If this set lies in the plane, then we obtain a plane geometric figure. But this answer would be too general—a "figure" in this sense would have no really interesting properties. The geometry of such figures would be almost devoid of theorems.

So it was first of all necessary to limit the class of sets to be studied, separating out those which had properties close to those of the ordinary geometric figures.

In order to separate out this class of figures we have to decide what it is that the ordinary figures such as the square, circle, line segment, astroid, etc, have in common. It turns out that we can construct all these figures by means of a single procedure.

It is said that when the famous sculptor Rodin was asked how he managed to make such remarkable statues, he replied: "I choose a block of marble and chop off whatever I do not need."

We can obtain any bounded plane geometric figure by this same method: we take a square which contains it and chop off whatever we do not need. Of course, we do not chop everything off at once, but proceed step by step, at each step removing circular pieces. Here we remove the interior of the circle, while its boundary, the circumference, is left in the figure.

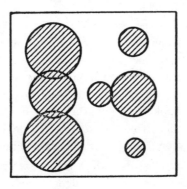

F<small>IG</small>. 40.

At first we might think that this procedure would only yield figures like those in Fig. 40. But the secret lies in the fact that we do not remove just one or two circles, but a countable set of circles. We can obtain any figure we like when we are allowed to cut out countably many circles. To do this we proceed as follows: take all circles both coordinates of whose centers and whose radius are rational numbers. The set of such circles is countable because of the Theorem 3.1 on p. 52. Next we remove from the plane all those circles of our set whose interiors contain no points of the geometric figure.

Clearly, only the geometric figure itself will remain after this operation, and the number of circles discarded is not more than countable.

However, we do not have to discard circles. Instead of them we could remove squares, rectangles, ellipses, observing only the restriction that the interior points are discarded while the boundary remains.

Continua

In addition to the ordinary geometric figures, it turns out that by means of removing a countable set of circles (or squares etc) we can also obtain other sets quite unlike the ordinary figures but still possessing many interesting properties. For instance, Sierpinski's carpet, of which we have already spoken at length, can be obtained in the following manner: from the square of side 1 discard small squares one by one, leaving their sides behind.

Moreover, by this discarding process we can also obtain "figures" not composed of a single piece. For example, if we remove "crosses",* as in Fig. 41, in the end we obtain a set not containing a single solid piece (said to be *completely disconnected*). Hence, we make the requirement that after

---

* Including terminal segments such as, for example, the segments *AB, CD, EF, GH*.

each discarding operation there must remain a set consisting
of a single piece. Then after all the removals there will remain

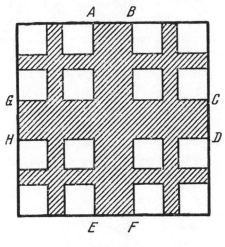

Fig. 41.

a set composed of a single piece (i.e., as mathematicians
say, a *connected set*). The set obtained will also be bounded,
i.e., it is entirely contained in some square.

A set *F* satisfying the following three conditions:

(1) the set *F* is obtained from a square by discarding a
countable set of circles (or squares etc), leaving their
boundaries,
(2) the set *F* is composed of a single piece (connected),
(3) the set *F* is bounded,

was said by Cantor to be a *continuum* (recall that the Latin
word *continuum* means unbroken). The continuum turns
out to be the most general set still possessing properties
quite similar to those of ordinary geometric figures.

Cantor Curves

Now we are in a position to answer the question: what is a plane curve? Since plane curves must be geometric figures, it is clear that we must search for them among the continua. But the square and the circle are continua, and we certainly do not want to call these figures curves. Thus, we have to add on some other requirement which would eliminate such figures.

Note that both the circle and the square contain "solid" pieces of the plane. But a curve would not contain solid pieces of the plane; no matter how small a square we took, there would always be points on it not belonging to the curve (Fig. 42).

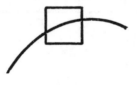

Fɪɢ. 42.

So here is the supplementary condition we need:

A plane curve in Cantor's sense is a continuum contained in the plane which does not fill any solid piece of the plane (i.e., in every square there are points not belonging to this curve).

For example, a segment, the boundary of a triangle, a circumference, a four-leafed rose are all curves. Sierpinski's carpet is also a curve; for in its construction we made holes in *all* the squares arising in the division, so that no solid piece of the plane is contained in it. Other Cantor curves

ınclude the circle with the spiral wound around it and the
saw-toothed curve of Fig. 43 together with the segment

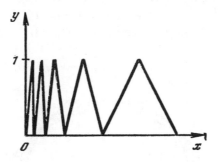

Fig. 43.

[0, 1] of the *y* axis. More generally, all those figures that
seem to our intuitions to be curves are also curves in Cantor's
sense, while any figure containing even one solid piece of the
plane does not belong to the class of Cantor curves.

But even among Cantor curves are some whose properties
are quite unlike those of ordinary curves. We shall now
discuss some of these.

Can the Area of a Curve Be Different from Zero?

Of course, now that the reader has made the acquaintance
of curves passing through all the points of a square, he will
not be surprised by anything. But even so, can a curve
have area? After all, Euclid did say that a curve is length
without width. And how can we get area from something
without width? In Cantor's definition of a curve, too, it
says that the curve cannot contain any solid piece of the
plane. Where will we find area in this case? But let us
not rush to give a categorical reply.

Before we study the question, we must come to an understanding about the exact meaning of the words used. What is meant by the words *"a curve has zero area"* or *"a curve has nonzero area"*? Let us take the most ordinary curve—a straight line segment. Since its width is zero, we can place it inside a rectangle of arbitrarily small area; we only have to choose a rectangle of sufficiently small

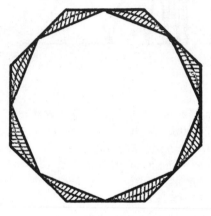

FIG. 44.

width. In exactly the same way we can put a circumference inside a polygon of arbitrarily small area. This can be done by inscribing a regular polygon with a very large number of sides and then circumscribing a similar polygon. The region included between the two polygons will have small area (the more sides our polygons have, the smaller the area), and the circle is entirely contained in this region (Fig. 44).

Now it is clear what is meant by the words *a curve has zero area*. They mean that no matter how small a positive number ε we take, we can find a polygonal domain which contains the curve and has an area less than ε. And if we cannot find such a domain, the area of the curve is not equal to zero.

In order to make the definition more clear we shall apply it to a more complicated curve than the simple segment or circle. Sierpinski's carpet represents, of course, a very complicated curve. Let us find its area. Recall first of all that the area of the whole square was 1. In the first step we discarded the central square of area $1/9$. We thus got a polygonal domain of area $8/9$. In the second step we discarded 8 squares each of which had area $1/81$. This left a polygonal domain of area

$$\frac{8}{9} - \frac{8}{81} = \frac{64}{81} = \left(\frac{8}{9}\right)^2 \qquad (4.27)$$

It is now clear that after the third step there will be left a polygonal domain of area $(8/9)^3$, then a domain with area $(8/9)^4$, etc. But if you take any proper fraction and raise it to higher and higher powers, the limit will be zero: if $0 < q < 1$, then

$$\lim_{n \to \infty} q^n = 0 \qquad (4.28)$$

In particular, $\lim_{n \to \infty} (8/9)^n = 0$. But by definition of limit this means that for any $\varepsilon > 0$ we can find an n such that $(8/9)^n < \varepsilon$. This tells us that after n steps we get a polygonal domain of area less than ε. And this domain covers Sierpinski's carpet. As a consequence of this, the area of Sierpinski's carpet is zero.

This would seem to mark the complete triumph of Euclid's definition. Even such a complicated curve as Sierpinski's carpet has area zero. But it would be premature to celebrate the triumph now. After all, no one forced us to discard such large pieces. Let us proceed more economically and divide the square into 25 equal parts, rather than into 9 (i.e., we divide each side into 5 parts). We discard the central square, whose area is, obviously, 1/25. Probably now the reader will want to divide each of the remaining 24 small squares into 25 parts and discard the central part. But this would again be uneconomical. Instead of this we take the segments bounding the discarded square and continue them until they intersect with the sides of the large square. This gives us 4 squares (in the corners) and 4 rectangles.

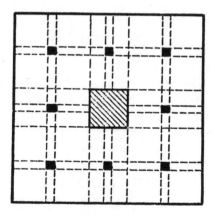

FIG. 45.

In each square and each rectangle we construct crosses with cross-pieces of width 1/25, discarding the central part of the cross (Fig. 45). Since the area of the central part is 1/625, the area of all the squares discarded in the second step is 8/625. Following this procedure, in the third step we discard 64 small squares of total area $64/25^3 = 64/15,625$

etc. The area of the discarded squares will now be given by the geometric progression

$$\frac{1}{25} + \frac{8}{25^2} + \frac{64}{25^3} + \cdots \qquad (4.29)$$

with multiplier 8/25. The sum of this progression is only 1/17. But what does this mean? This means that at each step an area of not less than 16/17 falls to the share of what is not discarded. So no polygonal domain of area less than 16/17 can possibly cover what is left. Now, this remainder, just as in the case of Sierpinski's carpet, is a curve (in Cantor's sense)—in constructing it we made a hole in every square and rectangle and not a single solid rectangle or square was left behind.

As a result, therefore, a curve in Cantor's sense can have nonzero area!

Domains without Area

Even so, the example we analyzed is not too convincing: the curve we obtained intersects itself everywhere and does not bound any domain. So the question arises: can a "good" curve that does not intersect itself, have nonzero area? It happens that it can!

We can construct such a curve by changing a little the construction carried out before. We first construct a set in which you not only cannot find a solid piece of square, but not even a solid piece of curve, and the area of this set will not be zero. To do this we have to discard whole crosses rather than central squares, as is shown in Fig. 46. Here we select the dimensions of the crosses so that the area of the first discarded cross will be 8/25, the area of all crosses discarded in the second step will be $64/625 = (8/25)^2$, the area of those discarded in the third step $(8/25)^3$ etc. Then

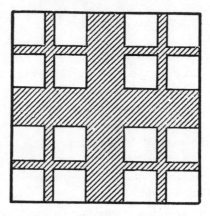

Fig. 46.

the total area of the discarded crosses will equal the sum of the geometric progression

$$\frac{8}{25} + \left(\frac{8}{25}\right)^2 + \left(\frac{8}{25}\right)^3 + \ldots \qquad (4.30)$$

i.e., $8/17$. But this is less than half the area of the original square. This means that an area of $9/17$ of the original square is left to the part remaining. Now in constructing the set we discarded whole crosses, ruthlessly tearing up the square. No two points of the set remaining can be connected by a curve, not even a curve in Cantor's sense; every connection between its points has been broken. As mathematicians would say, the remainder is a completely disconnected set. And still the area of this set, not containing a single piece of the plane nor an arc of a curve, is different from zero; you cannot cover this set with a polygonal domain of area less than 9/17.

Now it is easy to construct an example of a closed curve that does not intersect itself and has nonzero area. To do this we need only connect the points we already have just as we drew a curve through all the points of the square. And because we discarded whole crosses at each step, our curve will not intersect itself (in this it differs from Peano's curve). But since it passes through all points of the set, whose area must be at least 9/17, so the area of the curve obtained must be at least 9/17.

It is also no trouble now to construct a domain without area. For this we need only connect two points A and B of our curve with some kind of curve, perhaps a semicircle. Then we obtain a curve which bounds some domain G. And what is its area? The answer depends on whether or not we include the boundary with the domain—after all, the boundary itself has an area of at least 9/17. Clearly, our domain has no area in the ordinary sense of the word. In mathematics such domains not having area in the usual sense are called *nonquadratisable*.

Some Surprising Examples

It is probable that after the appearance of Peano's curve mathematicians were sure that they had already seen all the "miracles" that take place in the world of unusual functions and curves. But then their geometrical intuition let them down again. The properties of Cantor curves are so different from those of ordinary curves that we will do well to recount the following story.

At the beginning of the 20th century the well-known mathematician Schoenflies published a series of works in

which he discussed various properties of curves, the boundaries of domains, etc.   In these articles Schoenflies often
relied on "geometric obviousness."   But a few years later,
in 1910, there appeared a short (only 12 pages) article by
the young Dutch mathematician Brouwer.   It contained
several surprising examples, in consequence of which one
of Schoenflies' results was simply false and others, although
correct, were not rigorously proved.   In truth, some naughty
pranks were played on Schoenflies' "geometrically obvious"!

In order to show which "obvious" statements turned
out to be false we shall present some of Brouwer's examples
(we shall actually use some later simplifications).

Brouwer constructed a bounded domain whose border
was not a continuum.   In order to do this he took a "bottle"
and began to extend its neck, winding it around a circle
(Fig. 47).

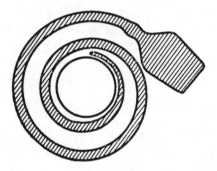

Fig. 47.

As a result he obtained a domain bounded by two spirals
and the "bottle."   But this boundary is not a continuum;
for in order to obtain a continuum we would have to add
in the circle around which the spirals are wound.

Domains and Boundaries

Since we have been discussing boundaries and domains, let us pause here to make these concepts more precise. After all, it turned out that Jordan's definition of a curve was not too successful, so that we need to give a new definition for a domain.

We shall call an *open set* in the plane, any set consisting of a sum of circles with their boundaries removed. In particular, the complement of any plane continuum is an open set in the plane. All the usual planar domains (the interiors of a circle, a square, a triangle, etc) are open sets (in the plane). In addition, these sets are connected; any two of their points can be joined by a broken line which does not leave the domain. These are also the properties that define a planar domain.

A planar domain is a connected set of points of the plane composed of a sum of circles with their boundaries removed.

Here the number of circles can be arbitrary. However, we can show that any domain can be composed from a countable set of circles.

A circle with its boundary removed is called a *neighborhood* of its center *a*. Of course, each point has infinitely many neighborhoods.

A point *a* in the plane is called a *boundary point* of domain *G* if every neighborhood of point *a* contains points of domain *G* as well as points not belonging to *G* (Fig. 48).

Open sets, domains and boundary points of domains in space are defined in exactly the same way. The difference consists in choosing spheres with their boundaries removed in place of circles with their boundaries removed.

In addition to the concept of neighborhood of a point (in the plane or in space) we shall need the concept of *relative*

neighborhood of a point belonging to some set A. That is
what we call the set of points of a neighborhood that belong
to set A, i.e., the intersection of an ordinary neighborhood
of the point with just the set A. For example, if A is the

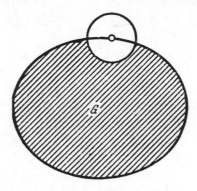

curve drawn in Fig. 49 and G is the neighborhood of
the point A, then the relative neighborhood of this point
is the arc of the curve between points b and c. If the
set A consists of several points, then each of its points
is a relative neighborhood of itself. In order to see

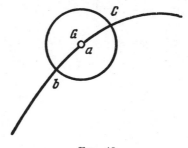

this, simply take an ordinary neighborhood of the point which does not contain any of the remaining points of the set (Fig. 50).

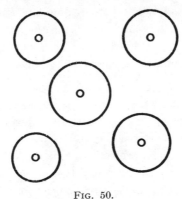

FIG. 50.

The Great Irrigation Project

We shall now talk about a second, even more surprising example of Brouwer. Let us draw the map of some country and the countries contiguous to it. Almost every point of the boundary of this country belongs to two and only two countries: the given one and one of its neighbors. On the map there are some points where three countries come together (Fig. 51). Three border guards stand at such

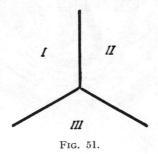

FIG. 51.

points. But there is only a finite number of such places on
the map.   And it seems quite obvious that such points
could not occupy the whole boundary of a country, i.e.,
that there could not be three domains (three countries)
sharing the same boundary.   In other words, it seems
obvious that three border guards from three different
countries will not be standing at every point of the boundary.

But Brouwer constructed three such domains. In order
to understand his example, imagine an island in the ocean on
which there are two lakes with fresh water. Only, one lake
is cold and the other is warm. Now we shall carry out the
following irrigation project. During the first day we
construct canals leading from the ocean and from both
lakes in such a way that each canal is "blind" (i.e., is only

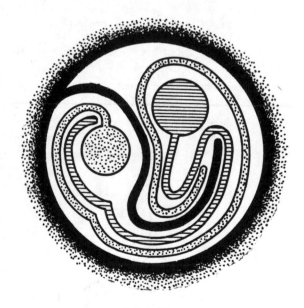

Fig. 52.

a creek of the corresponding reservoir), that the canals nowhere touch one another and so that, when we have finished, each point of dry land is at a distance of less than 1 kilometer from sea water and from the water of both lakes (Fig. 52).

During the following half day we extend these canals in such a way that they remain "blind" as before and do not touch one another, and so that now the distance from any point of dry land to any of the three canals is less than $\frac{1}{2}$ kilometer. In doing this, of course, the canals have to be made narrower than they were before. In the following quarter day we carry on, arranging matters so that each point of dry land is less than $\frac{1}{4}$ kilometer from any canal, etc. As we continue the process, the canals become ever more winding and narrower. After two days' work the entire island will be permeated by these three canals and converted into a Cantor curve. No matter what point of the curve we stand on, we can scoop up, according to our whim, salt water or warm or cold fresh water. And things are so arranged that the waters do not mix with one another. If we replaced the ocean and lakes by three countries, we would obtain the unusual map we spoke of at the beginning—three border guards, one from each country, could be placed at each point of the boundary.

A "Nondissertable" Subject

We already said that Cantor's definition had one fault— it was not at all suitable for curves in space. But then what is a surface in space? No one knew. This problem—to determine what curves and surfaces in space are—was put in the summer of 1921 to his twentythree year old student Pavel Samuelovich Urysohn by the venerable Professor

Dmitri Fedorovich Yegorov of Moscow University (it is evident that he thought a lot about the mathematical, significance of the problem or, as is sometimes said today, of the "dissertability" of the subject—this problem was one of the hardest!)

Urysohn quickly comprehended that Yegorov's problem was only a special case of a much more general problem: what is the dimension of a geometric figure, i.e., what are the characteristics of the figure which cause us to say that a segment or circumference has dimension 1, a square has dimension 2, and a cube or sphere has dimension 3? Here is what is remembered about this period in the life of P. S. Urysohn by his closest friend, a young doctoral candidate in those days and now an academician, the honorary president of the Moscow Mathematical Society, Pavel Sergeevich Aleksandrov: "... the whole summer of 1921 was spent in trying to find an 'up-to-date' definition (of dimension); P. S. shifted his interest from one variant to another, constantly setting up examples showing why this or that variant had to be eliminated. He spent two months totally absorbed in his meditations. At last, one morning near the end of August, P. S. awoke with his now well-known inductive definition of dimension in its final form.... That very morning, while we were bathing in the Klyaz'ma, P. S. Urysohn told me about his definition of dimension and there, during the conversation that extended over several hours, outlined a plan for a complete theory of dimension composed of a series of theorems, which were then hypotheses that he did not yet know how to go about proving and which were later proved one after another in the months that followed. I never again either participated in or witnessed a mathematical conversation composed of such a dense flow of new ideas as the conversation of that

August morning. The whole program outlined then was realized during the winter of 1921/22; by the spring of 1922 the whole theory of dimension was ready..."

The basic idea of Urysohn's definition of dimension consisted of the following. Two or perhaps several points usually suffice for separating a portion of a curve from the remainder (the part of the four-leafed rose of Fig. 53 con-

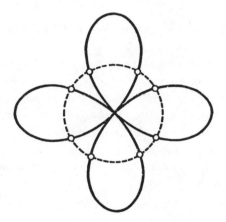

Fig. 53.

taining the center can be separated from the rest of the curve by using eight points). But it is already impossible to separate a part of a surface from the remainder by removing several points—for this you have to take a complete curve—no matter how many points you take on the surface, it is always possible to go around them. In the same way a surface is needed to separate a part of three-dimensional space from the rest of the space.

All this still had to be made more precise; for some curves an infinite set of points had to be taken in order to separate off some part, but the totality of these points still did not form a curve. Urysohn succeeded in giving a precise formulation to all the definitions required. In a way his definitions were reminiscent of those of Euclid (the ends of a curve are points, the ends of a surface are curves). But this resemblance is something like the one between the hollowed-out tree trunk of primitive man and a modern liner.

The Inductive Definition of Dimension

Let us now discuss more precisely how Urysohn defined the dimension of a geometric figure. A typical zero-dimensional set would be a set consisting of a single point or, in the worst case, of a finite number of points. But in such a set each point has a relative neighborhood with empty boundary—the point itself (see Fig. 50). This was the property that Urysohn took for his definition of a set of dimension zero.

More precisely, his definition went like this:

A set F has dimension zero, if each of its points has an arbitrarily small relative neighborhood with empty boundary.

In most cases it is possible to establish that a set has dimension zero by selecting for each point an arbitrarily small ordinary neighborhood whose boundary contains no point of the set *F* (then the boundary of the relative neighborhood is sure to be empty). But there are zero-dimensional sets situated in three-dimensional space for whose points such ordinary neighborhoods are not available.

The words "arbitrarily small" are inserted in the definition for the following reason. If these were not there, then we could, for instance, find a circle big enough to hold an entire square within it and so that no point of the square would lie on the boundary of the circle. So if these words were not in the definition, we would find that the dimension of a square is zero, not two as it really is.

In addition to finite sets, many infinite sets have dimension zero. For example, take the set of points on the x axis with coordinates $0, 1, \frac{1}{2}, \frac{1}{3}, \ldots, 1/n, \ldots$. It is clear that any point of this set has an arbitrarily small neighborhood that does not contain any points of this set. Only the case of the point 0 might cause some doubts. But if we take a neighborhood of radius α, where α is an irrational number, then no point of the set will occur on the boundary of this neighborhood.

The set Q of points on a line with rational coordinates is also zero-dimensional. To convince yourself of this, simply take an interval of irrational length centered at point a of Q as the neighborhood of point a. Cantor's set also has dimension zero (see p. 97) as is the set obtained by discarding crosses from the square (see p. 126) and many other sets.

We can similarly construct zero-dimensional sets in space as well as in the plane (in doing so, of course, we take neighborhoods of points to be neighborhoods in space).

After defining sets of dimension zero, Urysohn went on to one-dimensional sets, i.e., to curves. Here there are no longer small neighborhoods with empty boundaries (see Fig. 53). However, in the case of ordinary curves the boundary of the neighborhood only intersects the curve in a few points. But a set composed of a finite number of points has dimension zero. Generalizing this situation, Urysohn defined a set of dimension one in the following way.

A set F has *dimension one*, if it is not zero-dimensional and each of its points has an arbitrarily small neighborhood whose boundary intersects the set F in a zero-dimensional set.

It turned out that not only all the ordinary curves (circle, line segment, ellipse, etc) but also all Cantor curves have dimension *one* in Urysohn's sense. Thus, it now became possible to define the notion of a curve in space as well as in the plane.

A curve is a continuum of dimension one.

And it was also clear how to define surface, three-dimensional solid and, in general, a set of any dimension. Since the definition proceeds by numerical order, first defining a set of dimension 0, then a set of dimension 1, then of dimension 2, etc, Urysohn's definition of dimension is called *inductive*.

The Article Is to Be Printed, not Reviewed!

Urysohn proved many very interesting theorems relating to the notion of dimension that he introduced. But he was unable to find a way to prove one very important theorem; he could not prove that an ordinary cube has dimension 3. After prolonged effort he found a remarkable way out of the difficulty, conceiving a new definition of dimension in the process. We shall not discuss this definition in detail, but shall simply illustrate it on very simple figures.

If we take a segment or a circle, we can divide it into arbitrarily small pieces in such a way that each point belongs to at most two pieces (Fig. 54). Here we take the pieces together with their boundaries (i.e., their endpoints). But a square cannot be divided this way. It seems at first glance that if we divide a square into pieces, there will always be points belonging to four pieces (Fig. 55a). But if we place the pieces the way they lay bricks in construction work, we can do it in such a way that each point belongs to at

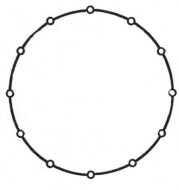

FIG. 54.

most three different pieces (Fig. 55b). In the same way, we can divide up the cube into small parallelopipeds in such a way that each point belongs to at most four parallelopipeds.

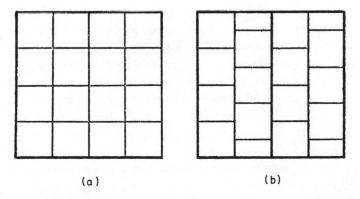

(a)   (b)

FIG. 55.

This is the property that Urysohn took for his new definition of dimension. A figure is said to have dimension n, if it can be divided into arbitrarily small closed parts in such a way that no point belongs to $n + 2$ different parts, but for a sufficiently fine subdivision there will be points belonging to $n + 1$ different parts.

The parts into which the figure is divided are not completely arbitrary; their complements must be open sets (such parts are called closed).

Employing this definition of dimension, Urysohn proved that the dimension of the square is 2, that the dimension of the cube is 3, etc. And he then proved that this definition is equivalent to the one given first.

Urysohn's theory of dimension made a great impression on the mathematical world. This is vividly expressed by the following episode. During a trip abroad Urysohn gave a report on his results at Göttingen. Before the rise of the Fascists to power the University of Göttingen was one of the leading mathematical centers. After the report the head of the Göttingen school of mathematics, David Hilbert, said that the results should be published in the journal *Mathematische Annalen* —one of the most respected mathematical journals of the time. A few months later, Urysohn again gave a report at Göttingen, and Hilbert asked the editor of Mathematische Annalen, Richard Courant, whether Urysohn's article had been printed yet. The latter replied that the article was being reviewed. "But I clearly stated that it was to be printed, not reviewed!" Hilbert exclaimed. After such an unequivocal declaration the article was soon printed.

For the next three years Urysohn carried on mathematical research unequalled in depth and intensity (during this time he published several dozen articles). A tragic accident abruptly ended his life—he drowned August 17, 1924 while swimming during a storm in the Bay of Biscay. He completed his last mathematical article the day before his death.

After Urysohn's death there still remained numerous rough drafts and outlines of unpublished results. His closest friend (and co-author of his many articles) Pavel Sergeevich Aleksandrov interrupted his own studies for a time and prepared these articles for publication, thus making these additional results of Urysohn available to all mathematicians. The theory of dimension at present constitutes an important chapter of mathematics.

Conclusion

Infinite sets possess remarkable properties. In studying these properties mathematicians were led to continually perfect their reasoning and to further develop mathematical logic. It was thought for a long time that the theory of sets and mathematical logic were abstract sciences having no practical application. But when electronic computers were invented, it turned out that their programming was based on mathematical logic, and many investigations previously thought to be remote from practical affairs acquired the greatest practical significance (this often happens in the history of science—even at the beginning of the 1930's a book could still be published saying: "Uranium has no practical uses.")

At present the theory of sets is fundamental for such areas of mathematics as functional analysis, topology, general algebra, etc. Profound studies are still being made in the theory of sets itself. These studies relate to the very foundations of mathematics. In these studies it has become clear that the "naive" approach to the concept of set that we took in this book is far from adequate. It has become necessary to axiomatize the concept of set. However, these investigations lie far outside the scope envisioned in the planning of this book.

Exercises and Examples

1. Set A consists of the integers divisible by 4, set B consists of the integers divisible by 10, and set C consists of the integers divisible by 75. What numbers are in the set ABC?

2. A library has books from various fields of science and art. Let A denote the set of all books in the library and let B denote the set of all mathematical books (not just the ones in the library). Characterize the set $A - B$.

3. Employing the rules of the algebra of logic, simplify the expression

$$(A + B + C)(A + B) - [A + (B - C)]A$$

4. What cardinal number is given by $2^{\aleph_0}c + \aleph_0 c$.

5. Set up a one-to-one correspondence between the points of the segment $[0, 1]$ and the points of the interval $(0, 1)$ (i.e., the segment with its endpoints 0 and 1 removed).

6. Prove that the set of points in the plane with both coordinates rational is countable.

7. Prove that you cannot find in the plane more than a countable set of mutually nonintersecting circular discs.

8. Find in the plane a continuum of mutually nonintersecting circular circumferences.

9. Prove that you cannot find more than a countable set of mutually nonintersecting figure eights in the plane.

10. Show that it is not possible to find in the plane a larger than countable set of curves having the form of the letter T.

11. Suppose that we have enumerated all the rational points of the segment $[0, 1]$. We obtain a sequence of points $r_1, r_2, \ldots, r_n, \ldots$. We construct a neighborhood centered at r_1 with radius $1/10$, a neighborhood centered at r_2 with radius $1/20$, a neighborhood centered at r_3 with radius $1/40$, etc. We sum up all the neighborhoods obtained. Will the set M thus obtained coincide with the entire segment?

12. Let the rational points be enumerated as in (3.9), p. 50. Produce an example of a point not found in set M of exercise 11.

13. We call the set of all sequences of real numbers $(x_1, \ldots, x_n, \ldots)$ such that $0 \leqslant x_n \leqslant 1$ the cube of countable dimension. Show that the set of points in this cube has the cardinality of the continuum.

14. Construct a continuous function that has infinitely many maxima and minima on each segment.

15. The set M consists of the points of the segment $[0, 1]$ which have decimal representations in which neither of the digits **3** and **8** occur. Describe a procedure for obtaining this set by discarding intervals from the segment.

16. Do the same for points whose decimal expansions do not contain the combination **38** (in the given order).

17. A point a is called the limit point of a set M, if in each of its neighborhoods there are an infinite number of points of this set. Show that all the limit points of Cantor's set (see p. 97) already belong to the set. Show conversely that all points of Cantor's set are limit points of the set. Do the same for the sets of exercises 15 and 16.

18. Show that each point of the segment [0, 1] is a limit for the set of all rational numbers such that $0 \leqslant r \leqslant 1$.

19. Does the set of integers have any limit points?

20. Prove that the complement of any open set in the plane contains all its limit points.

21. Prove that if a set contains all its limit points, its complement is an open set.